THE CATS

THE CATS

Joan Phipson

A Margaret K. McElderry Book

ATHENEUM

NEW YORK

1977

Library of Congress Cataloging in Publication Data

Phipson, Joan.   The cats.
"A Margaret K. McElderry book."
Summary: Two kidnapped brothers in Australia save
their abductors from destruction by a tribe of
feral cats that they cruelly abused.
[1. Kidnapping—Fiction. 2. Australia—Fiction] I. Title.
PZ7.P55204Cat   [Fic]   75-43608
ISBN 0-689-50061-0

THE CATS

CHAPTER

1

IT WAS A SUMMER'S DAY. He remem-
bered that. But whether he and Willy had been on their
way home from school or just mucking about in the
town he could no longer recall. Too many things
happened afterwards and the whole affair had become
like a dream (or, more accurately, a nightmare) and the
exact circumstances of its beginning hardly seemed to
matter. He was sure of one thing. They had been on
their way home, because it was on the outskirts of the
town that the car had come along.

If it had not been so hot they might not have been so
eager to take the lift when it was offered them, for they

1

had already almost reached the outlying plots of their father's plant nursery. Again, if the driver's face had not been familiar — one which he had seen often about the town — he might have thought twice about it. The appearance of the car was clear enough in his mind. But that could have been because he got to know it so well afterwards, inside as well as out. It was a large, black, old-fashioned car of the sort that looks as if it had been blown up from inside. It was shabby and two of the mudguards were dented, but there was still a certain dignity about it that must have given pleasure to its first owner. The dignity was still there at the end, which said a lot for the car, considering what happened.

If they had not been so busy talking about the money they would have heard it coming up behind them, for it was by no means a silent car. They would have been more aware of its slowing down and stopping. But they had thought of nothing all day but the money. After the mail had come that morning their mother, beside herself with excitement, had told them the amount of their lottery win. It was a figure they could hardly grasp. All they knew was that now boundless riches, enormous horizons, were theirs for the taking. Naturally they told everyone in the town. Another thing he no longer re-membered was whether their mother had said they were to keep it secret. She told them later that she had, but who could keep a piece of news like that secret? It blazed out of their eyes and burst like golden breath from their mouths. At least, it had out of his. He was the one who had told everybody. He always did the talking for Willy, and he naturally thought Willy would want people to know, just as he did.

So the car pulling up beside them caught them by surprise. When the door opened and Socker, smiling from the driver's seat, asked if they would like a lift Jim had only felt it was part of the beginning of the good times. He was hot, and he and Willy had already walked the best part of two miles. He got in, gratitude and happiness bubbling together inside him. Willy was slow to follow. Jim grasped him by the wrist and pulled him in too. The door slammed quickly behind them, Socker bent over the wheel and they were off, gathering speed as they went. It was only when they swept past their own front gate that Jim noticed Kevin had turned round in his seat beside Socker and was looking at him and Willy in a funny way. He knew Kevin from seeing him trailing round the town after Socker, an ingratiating smile always fixed on his face. There was no smile on his face now.

"Hey! Hold on!" The sound that came out of Jim's throat began by being loud and indignant, but he caught the look in Kevin's eye and the twist of his lips, and it faded into something like a whisper. "Where are we going?" he said almost inaudibly.

"You'll find out," said Socker without turning his head.

Willy lurched towards the door, and Jim thought he had been swung that way by the movement. But Kevin leaned quickly towards them and now, over the back of the front seat protruded a slim, blue-black rod.

"Sit still. He's got a gun," said Jim.

But Willy was already frozen, his eyes fixed on the barrel. After a long time, while Socker drove on and Kevin's fingers clutched the trigger, Willy's eyes slid from the gun to Jim's face. They were wide, terrified eyes and they were pleading for help.

"You don't have to point it at him any more," said Jim after a time. "He isn't going to jump, are you,

Willy?" Willy's head moved slowly from side to side. His eyes were on the gun again and they remained there, fixed, while his head moved.

"You wouldn't want to, the way we're travelling," said Socker. The speed of the car had increased and the last scattered houses of the town were flying past. The engine roared. The pistons crashed and screamed in the worn cylinders. Behind them the exhaust pipe belched half-used fuel. The steering column trembled. The back of Socker's head was motionless. He looked relaxed, and Jim could see one hand, large and broad-palmed, resting lightly on the steering wheel. But below, out of sight, his right foot must have been hard down on the accelerator.

The rifle barrel, accidentally or by design, was no longer pointed at Willy. It was now at a point about half way between them. Perhaps it was a kind of joke. Probably the pea rifle wasn't even loaded. Finding the sight of Kevin's pale, slack-mouthed face unattractive and the gun no longer menacing, Jim shifted his head slightly and studied the back of Socker's head and neck. It was a well-shaped head and a strong neck, erect and purposeful. The hair was thick, black and rather curly. It reached only to the nape and ended tidily. There was the same magnetic vitality in what was visible of Socker from behind that Jim had immediately felt and responded to in the smiling face that had invited them into the back seat. He recovered his confidence sufficiently to give Willy a smile and a little nod. Part of his life's work seemed to be protecting Willy, and he leaned forward now to give him a comforting pat on the arm.

"Cut it out," said Kevin and the barrel moved.

But Jim saw the sudden quiver in Kevin's lip as he

4

spoke, and the sight of the gun could no longer surprise him. Now that he did not think of it as loaded, its power over him was gone. It was only a hollow rod after all. And Kevin was afraid.

"Betcha it's not loaded," said Jim.

It was Socker who answered. "Want to find out?"

For a moment Jim held his breath. Then he said, "Anyway, that thing'll only fire one bullet. Then you got to load it up again. We've got a pea rifle at home."

From the movement of Socker's jaw muscles it seemed that he was smiling. "You're right," he said. "Kev'll only hit one of you. He can't miss, really. The only question is – which of you shall it be?" They were out in the open country now, and he stopped speaking while he turned a corner. "You want to decide?" he asked as the car gathered speed.

It was a game. They were getting at him, and in a little while they'd all be laughing at how he and Willy had been taken in. Before he answered Jim looked at Willy. It was no game to Willy. His face had gone so white it looked transparent — a different kind of white altogether from Kevin's. Willy never could understand being teased. It bewildered him and always ended by making him unhappy. Out of habit Jim swung in to his protection. "What's it all about, anyway?" he said, and he looked, not at Kevin, but at the back of Socker's head. "You're getting Willy all worked up. It's about time you told us."

"I'm going to tell you," said Socker. "But not now. We've got a way to go yet."

Out of the side of his eye Jim saw Willy looking at him. Again it was a pleading look. This time he knew Willy was asking not to be discussed. He never did like being talked about — seemed to think it was the same as

5

having the witch doctor point the bone. Willy took a bit of understanding.

The town was now out of sight behind them. Parchment-coloured paddocks, baking in the afternoon sun, lay for miles on either side. In the distance a green line of willows, divided by occasional big white-trunked river gums, wound its way along the course of a small creek. Ahead lay the junction where the highway to the city met them at right angles. Jim did not need Socker to tell him. At the junction he would know. If they headed for the city perhaps — perhaps it was no joke.

Kevin had slumped sideways in the seat. His hands on the rifle were slack and the barrel waved with the movement of the car. It seemed that Socker had eyes in the back of his head, for almost as soon as Jim had grasped the possibilities he said sharply, "You want to watch it, Kev." Kevin's eyes flew open. His long, spatulate fingers clutched at the rifle. It seemed, almost, that he would pull the trigger. "Just hold it easy," said Socker, and then appeared to concentrate on the road ahead where a spring washaway had left jagged holes in the tarred surface.

At the crossroads they slowed up. Cars were travelling at speed across their path. It was a busy road, and a fast road. There would be no time, very likely, to attract the attention of passing drivers. But there was a chance. Jim felt his muscles tighten. A pulse in his stomach began to throb. Then there came a gap. Faraway cars raced towards them from either side. Socker rammed in the gear and the black car shot on to the highway: on to it, and across it. They had not turned at all. Once over, the car's pace increased. The highway fell away behind them and ahead, hovering, it seemed, above the slightly rolling plain, hung the etched blue line of the hills.

6

"You taking us to the ranges?" Jim said. Surprise raised his voice to a shrill note.

"Any objection?" said Socker. Beside him Kevin gave a sudden giggle.

It was not what Jim had expected, and for a few minutes he battled with a feeling of sickness. But there was Willy to reassure, and he pulled himself together and turned towards him. Willy was already looking at him, and there was something in his eyes that stopped the gesture Jim had been about to make. He thought it was relief. Faintly puzzled, he said nothing and made no gesture.

"What's up?" said Kevin.

"What do you mean — what's up?"

"He looked at you kind of funny. What's he mean?"

"Better ask him," said Jim. "Then we'll both know." For no reason his confidence had returned.

"Well?" said Kevin aggressively, and waved the barrel towards Willy.

For the first time Willy spoke. "Didn't mean anything," he said in a high, clear voice. It was a tone Jim recognized. It meant Willy was living his private life.

"Here, you better —" Kevin had begun to shout and was drawing his knees up on to the seat when Jim heard Socker say, "Shut up, Kev." The sound was so quiet he almost failed to hear it, but Kevin subsided at once.

The car rattled and fumed towards the ranges and within it no one spoke. Inside Jim's head puzzled thoughts tumbled about. He might have guessed what was happening. He wondered later why he had not. But no one imagines the really exciting things happening to himself. They happen to other people, and then one reads them in the newspaper. He had forgotten that one exciting thing had already happened to himself and

Willy that day. Someone else would read about it in the paper. And soon, though he did not yet know it, someone else would read about him and Willy a second time. One thing, however, worked itself out in his puzzled mind. There was a connection between this road they were travelling, headed for the hills, and the look he had surprised in Willy's eyes.

This was the road, he now remembered with an inner jump of excitement, that Willy always took when he went off on his bike trips. Willy never said where he went, and they all believed he just went riding about. Sometimes he'd go off for days at a time with a bit of food and a billy and a blanket strapped on behind. At first their mother had worried, but she got over it when he always came back safely. But what if he always went to the ranges? What if there was something there, deep in the scrub, that Willy knew about and no one else did? He always came home looking — looking, their mother had once said, as if he might burst into flames. Just like a mother to say something silly like that. But it was a fact that at such times Willy had an appearance of floating just above the ground, and his eyes seemed always to be looking at something that wasn't there. Spooky. "Just been for a ride," he'd say in that same high, clear voice.

Then he thought that if Willy knew anything about the ranges it might be the same thing that Socker knew. Because why were they going there? Once they got into the scrub there was nothing for miles except rugged hills, trees and undergrowth, dead leaves and sticks and now and then a wallaby or an odd snake near the water holes. No one went by the old road any more, and the Shire Council had given up keeping it in repair. There was a notice somewhere to say so. Jim never came this way if he could help it. There was no fun being where there weren't any people. Willy might like prowling about on his own. He was always terrified in a crowd. But the football field was where Jim would rather be. A bit of life. A bit of excitement.

It was a kind of excitement he felt now, but a nasty kind, only made bearable by the thought of Willy sitting beside him with that new contented look. If only he knew. He looked again at Socker's head. Still quiet. Still confident, hunting the old car along as if he knew exactly what he was doing and why he was doing it. Socker was all right. Socker wouldn't — but there was Kevin beside him, and Socker must have wanted him there. Jim could have taken on Kevin by himself, alone, without Socker. Without the gun. Even if he *was* older. He wasn't much. Flabby and feeble. But not with the gun. With the gun he was vicious and dangerous. After what Socker had said, Jim could no longer persuade himself the pea rifle was empty. He knew that Kevin would enjoy using it if Socker ever gave him the green light. Jim had the sudden thought that none of the films he had seen, or the television shows he had watched, had told him what it meant to have a cove sitting pointing a gun at you. The cold, sick, frozen feeling was more like being ill than anything else. No fun at all. Not, when he came to think of it, even exciting.

The afternoon continued to flow past the windows. Shadows began to lengthen. The hard afternoon light was softening and turning yellow. Very soon they would start to climb into the ranges. The trees, dark and grey-green, rose up into the pale sky straight ahead. A crow rose, flapping lazily from the smeared remains of a rabbit on the road ahead. Jim heard it cawing as it flew away. With all his heart he envied it and wished that he

9

had been born a crow. Once again he glanced at Willy. Once again he saw with surprise that Willy had himself well in control, and what he was controlling — it became quite clear to Jim now — was excitement and even hope. He did not know why he remembered his mother's extravagant words: *as if he might burst into flames.*

2

W HEN THE SHADOWS of the first trees fell across the road Socker began to speak. "So you just won a lottery?"

The words were clear enough, but it was a second or so before Jim understood them. Amazingly, he had completely forgotten the lottery money which had so transformed his day until the very moment when Socker and Kevin picked them up. The knowledge came back to him now like a shield against whatever menace the immediate future might hold.

"That's right," he said eagerly. "Fantastic big lot of money." Willy made a sudden movement and perhaps

11

had been about to speak. But he did not. In fact, it was not necessary, for Jim knew the moment he had spoken that he should not have said it.

It was hardly a surprise when Socker said, "We heard. That's why you're here."

He knew it was too late, but he made one desperate effort to retrieve the situation. "Ever heard of a tall story," he said loudly. "Ever heard of a great, huge leg-pull? Eh, Willy?" He nudged Willy extravagantly in the ribs. "You been taken in, mister. You and your mate here, both." It had been a forlorn hope and after a time when Willy failed to respond, and when Socker made no reply but just sat there, driving, he said, "Anyway, how did you hear?"

Again the movement of jaw muscles as Socker smiled. "You didn't exactly keep it secret, did you? The whole town knew by lunchtime."

It was true. Jim remembered telling them in the pie shop. There had been a lot of people there, all buying pies. It had given him so much pleasure telling them. It had made him feel big and important. His heart shrivelled as he remembered it. He had known the news would travel. That was why he told them. But he said now — a last ditch stand — "Where were you, then? I never saw you."

Socker's broad shoulders moved very slightly upward and down again. "I heard," he said.

"So why are we here?" It was Willy who spoke. But they both knew the answer.

After a time, as if the moment were too good to relinquish, it came. "So your parents will pay it to me to get you back."

By now it had not needed to be said. Nevertheless, the words hung in the silence that followed, suffocating, dark and fearful. At the same time the sound and movement of the car changed as they came to the end of the tar and the tires did their best to grip on the loose gravel. The road narrowed. On either side the paddocks became uneven and were scattered with boulders and studded with briars. On the verges of the road the trees grew thicker, closed in, touched overhead and the golden sunlight was blotted out. They began to climb. Jim turned and looked through the rear window. Dust rose up behind them and settled softly on the glass and a yellow cloud swirled in their wake. Beyond it, half hidden by the trees, lay the cleared paddocks, spotted with red cattle, powdered with small groups of sheep. Beyond the paddocks, not so very far away, lay the town. Almost he fancied he could see the vivid green of his father's little nursery patch. The car swung round a corner, he lurched against Willy and the trees closed in behind them.

"Look to the front," said Kevin. But he must have thought the time for bolting was past, for the rifle barrel was no longer visible.

Jim turned again, settling himself with a kind of sigh. A glance at Willy had shown him that there was one problem he would not have to face. Willy was calm, withdrawn and, Jim had a queer feeling, a million miles away. Socker apparently had no more to say. He had not spoken since that last blunt statement, but started now to whistle softly to himself as he drove. Jim looked down at his own hands, each clutching a thigh, as if this grip alone would keep him safe. Familiar hands, shortish, useful fingers, broken nails, a scar here and there on the knuckles, brown on the back and not particularly clean. He looked at the scars, white lines in the brown, reminding him of the occasions when he had acquired

13

them. The homely circumstances of his life filled his mind again, restoring his sense of proportion, so suddenly shattered. Little by little the fingers round his thighs relaxed, lay lightly on the denim of his jeans, and rational thoughts began to organize his mind. He accepted at last the bald fact that he and Willy were being kidnapped for ransom. Somehow Socker was going to get a message to their father and, he did not doubt for a moment, his father would give Socker the lottery money. Then he and Willy would go home again. The adventure would be over. They would go on as they always did. Gradually a new feeling took possession of him. The fear and bewilderment dwindled. In their place grew a slowly mounting rage. Almost against his will his memory showed him the picture of that morning's breakfast table.

The table stood against the window in the kitchen. He and Willy sat side by side looking out of the window over the blue and white check breakfast cloth. Their parents normally sat at either end. This morning his father had been halfway through his final piece of toast and marmalade when they heard the postman whistle.

"You sit still and finish your egg," his father had said. "Or you'll be late for school. I'll go. I've nearly finished." Their mother had smiled and bent her head again to her plate. He remembered how the sunlight had shone on the well-brushed top of her head. Willy, as usual, was staring into space, absently poking cornflakes into his mouth. Jim had just put down his knife and fork when their father came in again, tearing open an envelope. Before he sat down he pulled out the letter and unfolded it. He took a long, long time to read it — so long that they had all stopped eating and were watching him when he finally lowered the letter and sat down slowly. There was such an increasingly stunned look on his face that their mother had eventually said, "Well, what is it? Have we won a fortune?"

He would never forget the way his father, wide-eyed and mouth half open, had slowly nodded his head.

"What?" his mother had said in her very highest register. In reply their father had passed her the letter across the table. By this time he and even Willy had quite forgotten breakfast and watched her as she began to read. He had half expected her to take as long about it as their father had, but he should have known she was made quite differently. Not two seconds after she had opened the letter she gave a gasp, crumpled it in her hand and sprang up. "Oh!" she said, and seemed to struggle for breath. "Oh! I can't believe it."

"We *have* won a fortune," Willy had said calmly. "How, Mum?"

It was the lottery ticket their parents had bought on the anniversary of their wedding day, and it was the first prize. He never remembered seeing his mother's face so blazing with excitement and happiness. She began telling them all that she was immediately going to buy for them: things, she said, that she had been wanting to get them for ages. It seemed to him that in the next ten minutes she had the whole fortune spent. Their father sat and beamed at her. He did not seem to want to say anything. After a while they had begun discussing the money more sensibly and Willy had remembered that school, unaffected by and oblivious of their news, would be starting at nine thirty as usual. Their parents had been still talking as they left the house.

Whatever happened they were not going to give that money to Socker.

The car was climbing steeply, following the line of a

creek up into the hills. The road was full of potholes and was crossed with channels dug and redug by succeeding rainstorms. Its surface was littered with dead leaves, strips of bark and branches brought down by winter gales. One could walk faster than the car was travelling now. It appeared likely that at any minute they might be brought to a dead stop. What then? If Kevin was careless with the rifle there might be an opportunity to break away. But Socker and Kevin would be after them at once, and he doubted whether he and Willy could run faster than they. There was a chance, perhaps, for himself. At fifteen and in good shape he might give Socker a run for his money. But Willy? It was just a fact that fourteen-year-old legs were not as long as the legs of someone — eighteen? nineteen? — Socker could be any age. It was already hard to imagine him being a boy at school. He must always have been master of any situation. He could have been a person to follow, even, if you did not happen to realize in time that he was going in the wrong direction. Kevin seemed happy enough — following. No one, surely, could like Kevin, yet here he was with Socker. So Socker liked him. He was Socker's friend. It was much, much, later than this that Willy, who never took much notice of people, said, "Coves like Socker don't have friends. They just have creeps following them." But at this stage Jim kept having to stop himself admiring Socker. He was an enemy and he would have to be fought, though looking at those muscular shoulders, the alert set of Socker's head, he knew there was little hope for a breakaway.

They were in among the hills now. All round them the bush rolled away for miles, kept empty, kept safe by the proclamation that it was a National Park and a sanctuary where any animal, bird or reptile, friendly or inimical to man might live in peace. It was a long time since any vehicle had passed this way and the noise of the embattled car had turned the birds mute. Even within the car they could feel a great silence in the scrub about them. The day was coming to an end. The sun, almost beneath a distant horizon, flicked the tops of the tallest trees in promise of a new day tomorrow.

"Where are we going?" said Jim.

"Just keeping you out of sight for a few days," said Socker. "I don't think it'll be too long, do you? Your dad's a kind-hearted sort of cove. When we tell him there isn't too much food where you are, I reckon he won't be too long handing over."

"You'll wreck the car, more likely. Then we'll all be stuck, food or no food." Anger began to loosen his tongue.

"I can nurse her through. You don't have to worry about that," said Socker.

"Through?" Willy's high, clear voice came unexpectedly.

"Sure. This road leads out into the country in the south — where they'll never think to look for us. I got it worked out. Don't worry."

"How do you know we'll get through?" said Jim. "The track could have washed away by now."

"Well it hasn't. I came through on a motor bike a while back. I told you I got it worked out." For the first time there was emotion in Socker's voice. He was angry.

From habit, when anything upsetting occurred, Jim looked round to check on Willy. To his surprise Willy was not in the least disturbed. Willy was not quelled at all. Willy sat there composed and very still, but his eyes were bright, moving from Socker to the bush around

17

them and back again to Socker. Jim looked away quickly so that Kevin should not see what he saw. Somehow, behind the stillness, Willy was changing. For the first time Jim found himself hoping, but for what he could not yet tell.

The sun had gone for good and beneath the overhanging trees the daylight was fading. The road ahead was becoming difficult to see. Socker, his spurt of anger forgotten, was leaning forward, peering ahead.

"Turn the lights on, why don't you?" Kevin said suddenly.

"And have everybody in the town wondering why there's a light in the scrub? Don't be more stupid than you have to be."

The car was going more slowly all the time. Presently when they reached a fairly level piece of ground they stopped. "Stay where you are," said Socker as he switched off the engine. "Kev, keep that rifle handy till I tell you." He opened the door and got out. Jim could hear shoes crunching the gravel. In the sudden silence the small sounds of the bush and the smell of warm eucalyptus leaves and dust came into the car. It was hard to see Kevin in the gloom, but Jim could just make out his eyes, and on the back of the front seat the rifle barrel gleamed. Willy leaned back in the seat, stretched out his legs and drew a deep breath.

"We're here," he said unexpectedly.

Socker walked to the back of the car and opened the trunk. When Jim made an effort to peer through the rear window Kevin said, "Look to the front." He seemed to get some pleasure from the phrase.

The trunk banged shut and Socker loomed up outside Willy's window. The door opened and he said, "Come out. You first." Willy scrambled slowly out of the car.

When he was on his feet in the road Socker said, "Turn round and put your hands behind your back."

Willy turned, held his hands behind him, and Jim saw that Socker held a piece of cord. He tied Willy's hands and when he had finished said, "OK. You can move off now. You won't get far like that and Kev'll be watching." He put his head into the car. "Now you."

There was little light, but enough for Jim to confirm his original impression of a strong, well enough looking face, marred only, when it was not smiling, by a downward turn of the mouth that suggested discontent and perhaps cruelty. But there was a firmness about the jaw and the chin muscles totally lacking in Kevin's.

Jim scrambled out. At the moment escape seemed out of the question, so he put his hands behind him. There was one faint hope, and he said, "What happens if I want to have a pee?"

"You tell me and I'll untie your hands, while Kevin here holds the rifle."

The faint hope died. He felt his hands being drawn together, felt the cord being pulled tight, and knew that Socker would tie a knot that would not slip.

"Now," said Socker. "You can walk about if you want, or sit down. But don't go too far. There'll be food in a minute. You get it, Kev. The carton in the trunk. It's wedged in beside that spare can of petrol." He stretched his arms, sighed and yawned. Then he looked about at the surrounding trees, the overhanging branches and the mauve sky above. There were no stars visible yet.

The road had come to a kind of wide saddle among the hills, and on either side of it a patch of sparse grass separated it from the trees. It was possible to see the darkening hills stretching away on either side. Jim stood in the middle of the road and looked back in the direction they had come, hoping to see some sign of the lights of the town. He would have found it a reassuring sight, but it was not there. The land rose behind them and trees blotted out the horizon. Willy had walked to the far side of the open ground and was standing with his back to them, his feet apart and his head high, as if he were listening.

At this moment, between day and night, Jim could hear no sound at all. The warm wind of the day had dropped and the leaves on the trees hung very still. All life — birds, insects, the small animals that lived in the undergrowth — had paused. Even the dust of their coming hung motionless in the air behind the car.

"What's he looking at?" said Socker.

"Better ask him," said Jim.

To his surprise Socker shouted, "Hey, you — Willy! What do you think you're doing?" When he stopped shouting a kind of echo, like the dust behind them, seemed to hang in the air. Still nothing moved, but somewhere there was a sense of shock. Then the echo — or perhaps it was merely the ringing in their ears — died, the sense of shock faded and the intense stillness flowed into the clearing again. Willy turned slowly and walked towards them. He did not speak until he was standing beside Socker. Then he said, "Nothing," very softly. There was hardly any daylight left, and he was standing pale and insubstantial as a ghost, his head on a level with Socker's shoulder. But Jim knew that something had happened to him. Standing there beside the trees, away from them all and the car, something had changed him. What had happened to him in the car when they first came into the scrub had happened again, only now much more. Jim knew that if he could clearly see his eyes they would be looking at something that was not there. Almost, he glimmered in the increasing dark. Jim looked quickly at Socker, wondering if he had noticed the change.

If he had, he made no sign. He only said, "Yes, well, you'd better stay here now so Kevin can give you the food. Sit down."

Obediently Willy sat on the grass beside the road. Jim sat beside him, and when Kevin thrust a meat pie under his nose, said, "What do you think I am? An octopus?" He saw Willy's teeth gleam in the darkness.

Then Socker said, "Give that to me and untie his hands. You'll have to eat one at a time. And stay sitting. If you try to get up I'll knock you over."

Laboriously they ate their meat pies. They were given bottles of soft drink, but Willy said, "I'd rather have water."

"Listen to him," said Kevin.

"There's no water," said Socker. "That's why we brought the drink. There'll be water later. Maybe that'll be all you'll get if your dad doesn't hand over the money pretty quickly."

"Where are you taking us?" asked Jim. It was a question that had been concerning him for some time.

Socker leaned back against a log beside him, spread his arms along it on either side and gazed at the pale stars. "No reason why we shouldn't tell you now. There's an old empty cottage the other side of these hills — looks south over the river. Been empty for years, I'd say by the look of it. You're going to wait there while I get a message to your dad."

"What makes you think we're going to wait?" said Jim.

"I'll be leaving Kevin — and the rifle," said Socker amiably.

21

"You got to be quick then," said Jim. "Kevin's got to sleep some time. What then? Think we'll stay and wait for you?"

"Reckon you'll have to," said Socker. "It's miles through the scrub and there's no water."

Jim remembered then that Willy had never gone off for long in the summer. His long trips had always been in the winter when there was water in the creeks.

"What about the river?" he said.

"There's cliffs between the house and the river. You'd have a long walk round. In any case —" He rolled over, brought his hands together and rested his chin on them. "Kevin will tie you up before he sleeps, like now. I got it pretty well thought out." The self-satisfaction — arrogance, even — was clear in his voice. Lying there, stretched out in the grass he looked formidable. Strong, compact, disciplined, he was an enemy who would take some defeating. Besides, Jim still felt this illogical admiration for him. A person to follow.

Out of the darkness came Willy's voice, high and clear. "Why have you got to take our money?"

Socker twisted and sat up. "Your money? You got no right to it."

"Have you?" said Willy.

"I've got as much right as you have. More. I need it. I got a right to a lot of things I never had. About time I began putting the record straight."

"What about Kevin?" said Willy. "Has he got a right to it too? Or isn't he getting any?" It was not like Willy to be provocative. Jim had never known him to muster the courage to needle anyone. But he was doing it now, without hesitation.

"Everyone's got rights. Even Kevin," said Socker. "He'll get his share. Don't worry."

22

"You just said we didn't have any rights."

Socker swung round to Willy and said savagely, "Why should you have rights? You've got everything you want. Home, parents to look after you, food, clothes, money in your pockets. Everybody nice and friendly wherever you go. No troubles at all. Why should you have rights? What have you ever done to have that much money dumped in your pocket? You don't even need it."

"That's right," said Kevin. "You don't even need it. Me and Socker, we need it."

Jim said quickly, "Needing it isn't the same as having a right to it. You didn't buy the lottery ticket. Mum and Dad did. Why shouldn't they have it?"

"Because I'm going to see they don't. Because I'm going to get it. Or you'll be sorry." There was a venom in his voice that left no room for doubt. He got up. "You two can sleep here. Kevin'll stay with you. I'm going to sleep in the car, just in case anyone thinks he can make off with it with his hands tied behind him."

"No one will," said Willy in his high, clear voice. "The road will be blocked. No one can go back."

Socker, half way to the car, stopped, turned and gave him a hard look. "You're mad," he said, and climbed into the car.

Kevin picked up the rifle, got up and walked to the other side of the log. For a few minutes he was busy kicking at the ground and pushing the dry grass about with his feet. Then he lay down with the rifle beside him. "Don't you try to be smart," were his last words that night.

Jim wriggled over to Willy, who was sitting bolt upright at the far end of the log. He intended to whisper what he could of comfort. But Willy turned to Jim before he had uttered a word and shook his head. His

23

face was in shadow, but his eyes were bright and very wide. It was Jim who received the comfort he normally gave. He nodded, sighed, and settled himself as best he could beside his brother, wriggling into the ground until he found a position in which he could relax. Once settled and his muscles going flaccid one by one, he realized he was deadly tired. Excitement, joy, fear, frustration in large quantities all in one day make demands on the toughest body. He knew that nothing would keep him awake now. Before his eyes closed he looked up at Willy.

Willy was still sitting straight as a ramrod, wide awake, with his head up, like a dog nosing new scents, on the brink, perhaps, of new experiences. From Jim's worm's eye view it seemed as if the whole night encircled Willy's head, the still, mild, motionless air wrapping him about as if it loved him. In the sky, large, bright and very far away, the stars were shining. All about them the trees stood, rank on rank, marching up the hills and down the slopes, shading the ground beneath, nursing the small things that flew, crept, or wriggled beneath them, guarding all the rolling country-side about them. An army, stalwart, and puissant, faithful to the trust, whatever it was, it had eons back in time been given. But silent and motionless. Ten million leaves hanging from a million boughs breathed silently in the night. Waiting or guarding. There was no saying which. The summer night hung, mild and tranquil, waiting too.

CHAPTER

3

A LIFETIME LATER Jim emerged
quite suddenly from dreams. All round him everything
was moving. Someone was shouting — but that was in
his dream. There was roaring now, not shouting. Sand
was being hurled into his face. It stung and it was
getting into his eyes. He pulled himself together and sat
up. The night was almost over. The trees, one by one,
were stepping out of the general gloom and were
standing erect, individual guardians of the clearing. But
they were no longer still. Their branches waved and
thrashed. The roaring he had mistaken for shouting was
coming from the leaves — the ten million tear-shaped

leaves — each twisting and leaping on its tiny stalk. It was dust from the road that was blowing into his face. Beside him Willy no longer sat, but stood with his feet together, hands still tied behind and his head raised in the wind, his pale, straight hair blowing about his head. The hot wind wrapped the jeans and shirt, flapping, against his body. Far overhead as the wild dawn broke, one blown magpie streaked across the sky.

The car door swung open and Socker came tumbling out, eyes wild and hair on end. He, it seemed, had been fast asleep, too. "What's happening?" he shouted. "What's up?"

Kevin, who had been oblivious to everything else, woke and got to his feet, snatching up the rifle as he did so. He stood, waving the barrel in great circles, drawing quick breaths through dilated nostrils.

"Put it down, Kev. You're dangerous." When he had done so, Socker stood, looking at the three of them. "What was it?" he said. "I heard a crash."

Willy looked at Socker and nodded. Then he jerked his head in the direction of the road. "Down there," he said. "Where we came. There was a tree fell."

Socker bent briefly to look into Willy's face. Then he turned and looked down the road. It lay, a pale streak in the half light. Jim felt a sudden stab at his nerve-ends as it appeared to undulate — to wriggle — where it disappeared into the darkness of the trees. Then he realized the moving trees and the blowing dust gave it that appearance. The road had not moved at all. With his back to him, Socker stood motionless. The black hair, which had blown clear of his face as he had leaned forward towards Willy, was now blown forward, making a white line down the back of his head as the wind parted it. It lay quivering close against the skull on either side. He stood silent and still for some time. Then he turned again slowly.

"I don't see it," he said. It was still at Willy that he looked.

"But you heard the crash," said Willy.

"How do you know that's where it was?" Socker seemed to have forgotten there was anybody there but Willy.

Willy, his eyes steadfastly on Socker's face, shrugged. "Wasn't it?" he said.

Jim saw Socker's eyes narrow, his mouth tighten, as he said, as if coming to a momentous decision, "I'm going to find out."

"Why bother?" said Kevin. "We been there already." It was not meant as a statement of fact. It was a plea not to be left alone with Jim and Willy. Kevin was beginning to show the whites of his eyes.

"I'm ;oing to see if we can get back if we want to." It was still to Willy that Socker spoke. Then he was gone, running down the road, blown by the wind, enveloped in dust. Very soon he was among the trees and out of sight. As soon as he was gone Kevin picked up the rifle.

"You sit down. Both of you." His voice was high and nervous. Looking over his shoulder and waving the rifle he walked to the car. Still looking at them he reached in, fumbled, and then withdrew his hand.

When he returned with the keys Jim said, "Think the car'll run away without us, do you?"

Kevin poked the rifle towards him. "You sit down when I tell you," he shouted.

Slowly Jim and Willy subsided against the log, their eyes on the rifle barrel. Willy leaned over and whispered in Jim's ear, "You got to treat him like an animal. He'll do things without thinking."

27

"Stop that," shouted Kevin at once. "No mucking about. You, Jim, get along to the end of the log."

Obediently Jim slithered farther away. He did not look at Willy again, but as he gazed ahead past Kevin's wavering form, past the weaving rifle to the mighty grey-green billows of the distant hills his mind was full of Willy. Everything about him was familiar, but to the familiar something had been added. There had become, somehow, more of Willy.

Socker was gone for perhaps fifteen minutes. While he was gone the sun, undaunted by the roaring sky and the moving land, pushed its way through the tree trunks, streaking the bush floor with rods of gold. The last of the night had gone, leaving behind its legacy of turbulence and unease. More birds whirled across the sky, shrieking as they flew. A few anemic clouds streamed overhead, diaphanous and touched with pink. The air was gritty with dust and smelt of dust. Leaves and twigs still battered their bodies and caught in their hair.

Socker came up to them in silence, walking hard, nostrils flared. They got up as he approached. He came straight to Willy. "How did you know?" he said. "How did you know there'd be a tree across the road? It only fell this morning. You told me last night." Once again he spoke only to Willy. He was not shouting, but there was something banked up behind the low voice that made Jim catch his breath and step back.

Willy blinked. A frown crumpled his forehead. "I didn't," he said at last. "How could I?"

Socker took a step forward. Jim saw that his hands were trembling. "You said we wouldn't be able to go back. How did you know?"

The frown deepened. "I just knew, that's all. How

28

could I know there'd be a tree? Last night there wasn't any wind."

Watching his brother's face, seeing the guileless, troubled expression, he knew that Willy was doing it again. It was a disconcerting way of Willy's to make comments, now and then, about things that had not yet happened. Usually it was something unimportant — there would be a letter in the mail, Mum was going to break a cup — they had given up trying to ask how he knew. He could never tell them and it bothered him if they seemed too surprised. It was accepted now as part of Willy. But it had shaken Socker profoundly. He could not understand, and where he could not understand he came out fighting. Jim saw his fists clench, and he prepared to fling himself forward. But Willy still had his hands tied behind him. He still gave Socker that worried, innocent gaze. And Socker swung round and made for the car, shouting, "Come on. Get in. We're going."

He waited, holding back the door while Jim and Willy tumbled in. Then he opened his own door, saw the keys were not there and caught Kevin by the arm as he made his way round the hood. "Where's the keys? Who took them out?" As if he had been electrocuted, Kevin shot his hand into his pocket and held out the keys. Socker snatched them and flung them on the seat. His face was suddenly red and swollen. "I'll teach you to take those keys without I tell you," he shouted, and brought the back of his hand across Kevin's cheek so that he fell face forward across the hood. When he got up his nose was bleeding and his cheek was fiery. But he went to his door and got in without looking at Socker again.

Jim knew the blow had been Willy's and he knew

now what Kevin was for. He knew why Socker put up with Kevin.

They drove all morning. It seemed that Socker had forgotten it might be necessary to eat or drink. All morning he did not speak, but sat crouched over the wheel, his eyes fixed on the road. Jim could not tell whether it was his mood or because the driving needed all his concentration. Whichever it was, no one dared break the silence. No one dared speak at all and each spent the morning with his own thoughts and wondered, from time to time, what were the thoughts of the three others.

Keeping the car moving along such a road and under such conditions was an undertaking that required skill and the utmost concentration. It was not only that the road was getting worse. It was as if there was a scheme afoot to prevent them getting on too quickly — sometimes, even, as if they were to be prevented from getting on at all. Walking — even pushing a bicycle — would have been quicker. The wind still blew. The trees raged and thrashed, hurling twigs, leaves, bark and even branches around them as they struggled ever upward and onward into the virgin scrub. Into the protected, primitive land. The sun rode high above, over the trees in a pale and distant sky from which all the early wisps of cloud had been banished. The day had become hot, strident and glaring and the inside of the car was slowly dehydrating all four of them, for their speed was not sufficient to create a flow of air. The engine, in low gear, groaned as it pushed the wheels round. The wheels scrabbled and scraped on the uneven gravel and plumped into the dust pockets. The number and depth of the waterworn channels was increasing as the road grew steeper. The potholes could not be avoided and the engine became more agonized as it pulled the car out of one after another. They stopped once for an hour because the petrol began to vaporise. Apart from that they somehow escaped trouble. None of the heavier branches had so far hit the car. No tree had so far fallen either on them or ahead of them across the road. It was as if they were being allowed to proceed deeper and deeper into the bush, but not without labour, doubt and strife.

About midday Socker stopped the car. When it came to a standstill he switched off the engine and flopped forward across the wheel with his forehead on his hands. Still no one spoke or moved. Now that the car was silent the sounds outside poured in through the open windows. The bush was roaring still, and above the deep, hollow notes of the wind in the gullies the shrill screaming of the treetops added a note of hysteria to the general hubbub. The sun blazed down, implacable and searing, and the west wind carried with it all the parched heat of the central Australian deserts. The birds of the morning were silent and invisible now, beaten down by the cruel day. Like the occupants of the car they cowered, nerves stretched, in whatever cover they could find.

Presently Socker moved. "You can get out," he said. Then he threw the car keys to Kevin. "You go to the trunk and get the food," he said, and slumped again across the wheel.

They sat on the ground on the shady side of the car, partly protected from the wind and ate pies and drank bright green soft drinks.

"However many pies?" said Jim.

"Enough," said Socker. "You eat. We got to get on." But he seemed in no hurry. As soon as he had finished his pie he rolled over on his stomach and rested his face

31

on his crossed hands. Perhaps he thought escape was no longer possible, for he fell immediately asleep. They ate their pies and drained their bottles, and they were still thirsty, for soft drinks are no substitute for water.

Jim and Willy had been allowed to have their hands untied while they ate, but Kevin sat facing them, the rifle beside him. When he had finished his pie, Jim watched him, for Kevin was unpredictable. He sat now, upright against the rear wheel, alternately watching Jim and Willy and throwing uneasy glances at Socker's unconscious body. The wind had made them all jumpy, but Kevin looked as if he might snap at any moment. He was not happy and he was afraid. Across his cheek the red mark of Socker's hand was still visible and there were smears of blood about his nose.

"We can't go much farther without a drink of water," said Jim. It was a true statement, but he wanted to see how Kevin would react.

Immediately he said, "Sh!" and looked at Socker. It was not the reaction Jim had expected, but it was revealing. Seeing that Socker slept on, Kevin said, in a kind of rough whisper, "You'll get water when he gives it you. Not before. You got to wait. Same as us."

Willy moved his back a little against the car door. "There's a creek a bit farther on," he said. "Once we get on the ridge there's a spring and a bit of a creek across the road. Sometimes it's running, even in summer."

Jim shifted until he was looking Willy full in the face. "You know?" he said. "You been this far?"

Willy nodded and gave his brother a little smile. "I know it all," he said. "Well."

"What's that?" said Kevin, for the wind had drowned Willy's voice.

"Nothing," said Jim. "Just talking to me brother,"

and he settled down on the ground and closed his eyes. Somehow, things were looking up. He had his first vague feeling that relationships were changing. Even in the middle of this hellish day there was hope about.

It was Kevin who woke Socker in the end. Jim had gone to sleep, Willy had remained sitting with his back to the door, his eyes on the remote distance and his consciousness withdrawn too, to some deep and personal well of contemplation, and only Kevin continued aware of the wind, the beating sun and the angry trees. Half way through the afternoon he flicked a twig at Socker's head. It hit him over the ear and he woke, scratching the place. He saw Kevin observing him.

"You was hit by a twig," said Kevin. "It's getting on. Think we better go?"

The sun had crossed the road and the shadow they sat in was receding. Socker sighed, looked carefully at Jim, asleep beside him, and Willy deep, it seemed, in thought.

Jim woke with a shoe in his backside, not painful, but firm. He got up. Kevin came up with a cord. "Do we have to?" he said to Socker. "Do we have to have our hands tied? How could we get away now?"

For a moment Socker met his eye. It seemed he was going to give Kevin the order. Then his glance swept towards Willy. Jim saw the eyes narrow, the jaw clench. "I reckon you have to," said Socker. "Get on with it, Kev."

So again their hands were tied and again they were bundled into the back of the car, and they proceeded on. It was the hot period of the afternoon and after the pie and the sickly drink Jim felt even sleepier. There was no point in struggling to keep awake, and he let himself sink into a stupor, half sleep, half swirling, unreal thoughts. And the time passed.

When he opened his eyes again, the air in the car was cooler. The sun was below the level of the treetops and they drove in blessed shadow. But something else had changed. He did not move, but looked at each of the others in turn. Willy, beside him, was sitting placidly as he had sat since they first got in. His eyes were bright and calm and he looked, as he always looked, far ahead, at the road and the trees beyond and the distant sky beyond the trees. Kevin, directly in front of him, was sitting well down in the seat, his head sunk between his shoulders. Either he was asleep or he was trying to draw as little attention to himself as possible. The rifle was propped against the seat beside him, and Jim could see the tip of the barrel leaning against the door. In front of Willy, Socker sat as he always sat, his hands in the same position on the wheel, shoulders resting against the back of the seat, strong head and neck alert and determined.

But it was Socker who had made the change. Jim knew at once that Socker was different. Perhaps it was that the strong hands now had a tighter grip of the wheel. Perhaps it was that the neck muscles had become more rigid. Perhaps it was the glimpse he had of that telltale jaw muscle — taut now, where it had been relaxed before. But most of all, he now realized, it was in the sound of the engine and the movement of the car. Socker was driving more recklessly, and he was fighting the car instead of nursing it. Where, earlier, he had pressed it, forcing the engine to its maximum, now he asked too much of it and by the different sounds it made Jim knew that it was rebelling. From time to time the wheels skidded and spun in the loose gravel. They were driving harder, but their progress was diminishing.

The sun was already on the horizon when they reached a small plateau and came to the little creek that

34

Willy had known was there. The culvert where it crossed the road had long since been washed away and it had dug a rocky channel for itself through the gravel. A trickle of clear water ran through the channel. It was the best sight Jim had seen all day. As they drew near, Socker slowed the car. Assuming they would stop, Jim sat up, preparing to get out. He had tried to forget he was thirsty, but the sight of the trickle of clear water reminded him again forcibly. The slackening of speed and the changing of gear attracted Kevin's attention and he sat up.

They reached the creek, Socker changed into bottom gear and began to guide the car over the boulders.

"Hey!" shouted Jim. "Stop. I want a drink." Backing himself against the door he fumbled with his tied hands for the handle.

For once Kevin was on his side. He flung his own door open and tumbled out onto the road. Before Socker had stopped the car he had his face in the water. The rifle lay where he had knocked it, inches from the creek.

There was no choice, and furiously Socker rammed on the brake and switched off the engine. The car steamed and clicked as they got out. "Go on then. Hurry," he said, and made for the running water. Socker had not thought to untie Jim and Willy, but it was not necessary. They were too thirsty to care, and they flopped on their stomachs in the road and plunged their faces into the creek. Socker was on his feet first. "Come on," he said. "We got no time."

Jim sat back, his face dripping. "What's the hurry? You got an appointment somewhere?"

For a minute he thought Socker was going to hit him, too. But Kevin, getting to his feet and picking up the rifle, said, "We're not going to get far tonight, Socker.

35

The light's going already, and if we can't use the headlights . . ." He stopped and then seeing Socker was not going to attack him, said quickly, "Why can't we stay here where there's water?"

"Because we should have got there tonight. That's why." It burst out of Socker as if he could hold it back no longer. "Didn't you see? We've been going slower and slower and slower. We should have been there by now. I can't get her along somehow." He stopped and looked at the car as if it were an enemy. "What's happened? I dunno. If took me half a day — *half a day* — to get back on the bike. We've been a day and a half already. You tell me why. Go on. Tell me why." He took a step towards Kevin, who backed quickly away.

Willy had been climbing slowly to his feet and now, wiping his face on his arm, said quietly, "I know the house where you're taking us."

He was going on, but Socker interrupted in a voice as quiet as Willy's. "And what do you know about it?"

"I know it," said Willy. "That's all. You'll never make it tonight. It's a long way and they won't . . ." He stopped, drew a breath and then said, "You won't be able to get on too fast. The road's bad." The final comment came as an afterthought — as if he had not really meant to say it.

Socker said, watching him closely, "What about the bike? How did I get back so quick on the bike?"

"Downhill," said Willy, and turned away.

Watching Socker, Jim could tell that he was uneasy. If it was the house Willy seemed to know about, he had reckoned on reaching it much sooner. This was why he had been driving as he had. This was why the atmosphere in the car had been one of frustration, of fires banked but growing fiercer.

36

"It was as if I'd been held back. All the way I been held back." He was not speaking to anyone in particular. It came out of him as if he had been thrashing it out in his mind all afternoon.

"Anyway, I don't see why we can't go on." This was Kevin, trying to say words that would please. "We could turn the lights on. They'll never see us now."

"You fool. It's now they'll be looking for us. It's now they'll have everything out, searching. How do we know they won't use helicopters? We should have been under cover by now."

Kevin's words had failed to please, and he recoiled like a snail in salt. Jim was about to say that no one would yet know they had been kidnapped, then held his tongue, remembering in time that soothing Socker was not necessarily in his own best interests. But it was significant that the plans had been revealed to this extent. He was not surprised Willy knew about the house. He was now prepared to believe Willy knew the whole of this area stone by stone and tree by tree. He suspected, too, that Willy travelling by himself, even pushing the bicycle, would have made better time than Socker's car. Willy would know the short cuts, over ridges and across gullies, where the road could not go. The difference was that Willy knew better than to risk the long distances in the heat of summer when the creeks were dry. People lost in the scrub had died for this mistake.

CHAPTER

4

IN THE END they spent the night there, leaving the car on the brink of the creek and moving themselves a little way up the bank to where there was a patch of green grass. Socker allowed them to spend the night with their hands untied, perhaps thinking that there was no escape from here but by car, and no one would willingly leave the water now it had been found. By the time Socker had finally made up his mind the day had almost gone. It was only then they realized that the wind had dropped. With the dying wind had gone too the stress and strain of the day. The trees, after their violent movement of the past twelve or fourteen hours, stood, battered and weary, their branches drooping like tired horses. Furtively, as the light died, small night noises began. Frogs along the creek struck up their resonant drummings, intermittently at first, and then in full throated harmony, reverberating in the ear drums, palpitating on the night air. Night birds began to hoot and creak and somewhere far away on a western hillside a kookaburra gave a few hesitant chuckles and stopped.

They were sitting all together on the grass, finishing the last of their pies, like any ordinary picnic party.

"Got any more pies?" said Jim.

"Nope," said Kevin. "If you're still hungry you gotter go without."

"I'm not hungry, thanks," said Jim. "I was only thinking they were getting pretty tired. Mine had just died, I think."

Socker lay back, his head on his hands and his eyes on the sky. He seemed to be relaxing. Perhaps it was time to talk. "You got a telephone in this house of yours?" asked Jim

Socker's eyes flicked from their contemplation of the sky to where Jim sat beside him. "Maybe," he said. "Why?"

"Just wondered how you'd ask Dad for the money. It's a long way to walk back."

Socker made no reply, but Willy said, "There's no phone. It's just a wreck. Been empty for years. Matter of fact it's been . . ." He stopped and turned away and presently he began to whistle softly to himself.

"Been what?" said Kevin.

"Nothing," said Willy, and he began to look at the trees that surrounded them as if, Jim thought, watching him, there was some message there for him.

Presently Socker said, "You don't have to worry. I've

got it all worked out. And I wasn't planning to go back. I don't mind telling you because it doesn't matter if you know. I'll be ringing your Dad from a little place I know the other side of the river. He'll never know where the call's come from. Not the way I'll do it." Jim heard the pride in his voice. From that time on he began to understand that Socker needed an audience. He required admiration. This need was the basis of most of his actions. Now, he was waiting for an answer. He was waiting for the right answer. Kevin did his best to provide it. This, too, was what Kevin was for.

"You thought of everything, I reckon, Sock. Just like the big shots on the T.V."

It was not Kevin's answer that Socker wanted, and when Jim failed to make any comment he gave a snort and turned over on his stomach. Out of habit Jim glanced round to check on Willy. He had not been as disturbed over recent happenings as Jim would have expected, but one never knew with Willy. He could look calm and still be in a terrible state inside. At this moment he was staring at the road just behind the car. When he saw that Jim was watching him he looked away and resumed his study of the trees. For Willy, it was a furtive movement, and Jim looked quickly at the same bit of road. Something gleamed in the half light by the water's edge.

"Look," said Jim. "Your pea rifle's nearly in the water." And he knew as soon as he had said it that Willy had wanted him to keep his mouth shut. Why couldn't he learn to think before he spoke?

Jim had spoken to Socker, but it was Kevin who said, "It's mine, not his."

"You better get it then," said Socker lazily. "We could still need it."

Kevin sighed and got up. When he sat down again with the rifle beside him Socker said, "Now unload it and give me the bullet. Then go and get the packet of ammunition from the car. And give that to me, too."

Kevin said, "You get it." But he pulled back the bolt and took out the bullet just the same. Then, when Socker seemed not to have heard, he got up again, went to the car and fetched the packet from the glove box. He slipped it into his pocket and was going to sit down again when Socker said, "Give it to me, I said." For a moment he hesitated, then he went to Socker and dropped it on the ground beside him.

Socker looked at it, then up at Kevin, who still hesitated. Then he picked the packet up and slid it into his trouser pocket. "That's right, Kev," he said amiably. "We wouldn't want Jim and Willy to get their hands on a loaded rifle, would we?" When Kevin failed to reply he said to Jim, "See, Kevin, he likes to be bossed about, don't you, Kev? He's got a mum that'd scare the daylights out of me any time. Scares them out of your dad, too, doesn't she, Kev? And all your brothers and sisters. Don't know why you put up with it, myself."

Goaded, Kevin said, "I don't put up with it. I'm here, aren't I?"

Socker nodded. "That's right. You got away. You know a good thing when you see it, don't you, Kev? And you saw me. And now look where we are. Rich, almost."

Jim remembered then where Kevin fitted. His mother was a forceful, public-spirited woman, very active, very efficient, who was president of — something or other. His own mother had once told him of what. Kevin's father did something in the town council chambers. Kevin did have several brothers and sisters. Some were at school with Jim and Willy. They were all subdued and not very clever. Kevin must be the eldest. No wonder he found Socker a change. But, as Socker said, he'd have to follow and, Jim could see that in some strange way he enjoyed being bullied.

Some minutes went by after Socker finished speaking, then Kevin said, "Anyway, it's my gun." After that no one spoke any more.

They were all tired. The night was calm and the air soft and tranquil. The grass they lay on was cool. The encircling trees stood well back from their patch of grass, so that they did not at all have the feeling of being surrounded and brooded over. The trees, indeed, were so still, so silent they could have been sleeping too. All nature was resting after the torments of the day. They should have slept dreamlessly the night through, but it did not happen quite like that.

Jim was already halfway to sleep when he sensed a movement. He opened his eyes. In the faintly luminous darkness Willy was moving. He got to his feet and walked away towards the trees. He made no noise at all, but Jim could not tell whether this was by design or because Willy's movements were always quiet and economical. As he retreated he became harder to see. By the time Jim reckoned he would have reached the trees he had vanished altogether. Jim sat up on his elbows, peering. He could not tell if Willy had gone in among the trees, away from them all, or if he was still at the edge of the clearing, waiting. Waiting? It was a funny word to come into his head.

He was still wondering whether he should follow, whether Willy was going to need him, when he heard a movement on his other side and an interruption in Socker's regular breathing. He knew that Socker was stirring, too. He understood at once what he should do.

He must cover up for Willy if it became necessary. Socker, it seemed, was holding his breath, and Jim guessed that he was listening for the breathing of the other three. Then he sat up quickly and Jim saw the gleam of his wide open eyes as they moved from one dim recumbent figure to the next. When they reached the place where Willy should have been he heard Socker's breath drawn quickly between his teeth. Socker was getting to his feet. Then he said loudly, "Where's your brother? Where's he gone?"

The sudden sound went ringing round the clearing, shattering the silence. Jim thought, queerly, that the trees quivered. It silenced the frogs and even, it seemed, the small gently humming insects. Only the creek continued its poppling as if nothing had happened.

It was not possible to see to the edge of the clearing, but when the last vibrations of the sound had died away Willy's voice came out of the darkness. It was not strident as Socker's had been, but clear, thin and in tune with the silence. The frogs, which had resumed again, took no notice. The insects hummed on. "I'm here. What's the matter?"

"You come back here. I never said you could go right over there." Some of the alarm had gone from Socker's voice.

"It's more comfortable. I can't sleep there."

"You come back here." Jim thought Socker would go bounding over to where Willy was. But something — some indecision — held him back. "You come here," he said again.

"I like it here," came Willy's voice again. "I think I'll stay. If you come over I can go into the trees. You'll never find me." Jim could hardly believe what he heard. This could not be Willy speaking. But, yes, it could be

Willy as he now was — as he had become since they climbed into the hills.

As Socker stood momentarily puzzled and silent, Kevin jumped up. "I'll get him for you, Sock." Eager to please. Eager to prove his value.

"You shut up and stay where you are." But he had made Socker's mind up for him, for Socker said now, "You, Willy, you going to stay there all night?"

"Yes," came Willy's voice like a sigh from the darkness.

"How do I know?"

"You don't think I could run away, do you, Socker? Where would I go? You've got us caught, Jim and me." Jim knew it was mockery. There was a Willy speaking he did not know. It was a Willy who no longer needed Jim's protection, who had assumed a confidence that did not require protection. Jim wondered if it had been there all the time, smothered.

There was nothing Socker could do but agree and he did so, saving as much pride as he could. "OK then. But if I find you've moved an inch into those trees in the morning you'll be sorry."

"Oh, the *morning*," said Willy. And then, "Good night, Socker." There was no more sound. Not even the sound of Willy lying down, or turning over, or crumpling dead leaves with his body. There was just no more sound.

Socker lay down. Jim heard him turn a few times, heard his breath come unevenly for perhaps ten minutes, and then resume its slow, long rhythm as he slept. It was some time before Jim could go to sleep again. Knowing Willy was out there on the edge of the scrub by himself, away from the rest of them, was strangely exhilarating. Again the hope he had felt before

44

began to bubble inside him and he lay, looking upward, wondering, thinking that if this were an ordinary night he would be in his bed, unconscious, as good as dead until the morning. But up here the trees would still be standing, the creek still poppling and above, as above his own house, the sky he looked at now would still be there, the stars would still hang, scattered in space over his head. He looked up at the stars. They were very bright. High above, far in the coal black sky, they blazed with the light of distant suns. They could not be there for nothing, so many of them, cast about like a broken necklace all over the place. He had been told at school how they came to be there — more or less. But no one had told him why, and suddenly this was more important. If he knew why they were there, perhaps he would know it all. The change in Willy would be explained and, for the matter of that, the change in himself, too, having these queer thoughts in the middle of the night. Socker would be explained. But Socker needed less explaining all the time. Again the *how* was clear but not the *why*. As he gazed and the thoughts came and went, he saw one of the stars moving. A shining pinpoint in the blackness, it described a great arc in the sky, from west to east, moving through the other stars until it sank, pursuing its undeviating way over the eastern rim of the world. He thought at first it was a comet, but it was too unassuming with no tail, no blaze of light. It had, somehow, no celestial status. Then he knew what is was. It was a satellite — a man-made satellite — probably bouncing football games from one side of the world to the other. And it, too, shone in the light of a distant sun. It too, had its place in the sky. He sighed and shut his eyes, and dreamed of stars and trees and parents and rushing winds — and sleepy animals, purring, wailing, speaking in animal voices in the bush.

He did not know how many hours afterwards his eyes flew open and he sat bolt upright. The purring and other faint sounds were still in his ears. He peered into the darkness where he had last heard Willy's voice. It seemed to him the sounds had come from there. He was about to call out, but paused, finding himself reluctant to wake the other two beside him. The sounds had not been alarming. They had been placid, sleepy sounds, not meant to harm. And if it had been purring, there was no harm in that. He listened, holding his breath. No sound came. Only the splash of the creek and a few frogs, still doggedly croaking the night away. There was no sign yet of daylight. There was no wind at all. It was the very depth of night, and utterly silent. Then, his ears straining, he heard a small sound. It was a breath, a sigh, a kind of crooning. And it came from where Willy slept. He would know Willy's voice anywhere. He lay down again, reassured, and when his heart had resumed its normal beat he slept again.

The next time he opened his eyes it was because of Kevin. The night had gone, and it was the white light of early morning. Kevin was standing on his feet, shouting and pulling at Socker's arm. As Jim sat up Socker woke, saw Kevin standing above him and said, in a voice still thick with sleep, "What's biting you? What's wrong?" Then he looked quickly across the clearing to where Willy should be. Seeing him lying there, his back against the nearest tree, with his eyes closed, Socker wrenched his arm from Kevin's grip and said, "Shut up, can't you?"

Kevin let go his arm and took a deep, trembling breath. His face was whiter than usual. "I heard someone scream," he said at last.

Jim was sitting up now, and Socker looked from him

to Willy and back to Kevin. "You're mad," he said. "Nobody screamed. You must have dreamed it. Go back to sleep. It's too early yet." He lay down, rolled over in the grass and seemed to sleep at once. Jim watched Kevin as he slowly subsided. His glance kept roaming round the clearing and his nostrils were still dilated, but he lay flat at last, though not before Jim had heard him mutter to himself, "But I did hear it. There was a scream."

When they stirred the sun was
up. The day had begun and all was normal. It looked
like being a much better day than the one before. There
was a small breeze, but nothing like yesterday's gale,
and overhead a few white, scattered clouds gave depth
and colour to the blue. It was going to be hot, but now
the air was fresh and smelt of eucalyptus and wet earth
and the small aromatic herbs that grew along the creek
bank. The frogs were silent, but the birds had begun,
and a great singing, chirping, laughing and shrieking
filled the morning sky. Bees, wasps, beetles and flies
hurried through the golden air. Spiders dragged their

silver threads from leaf to leaf. It was already a busy day.

Willy looked as if he had spent the night in a comfortable bed safely in his own home. He glowed with well-being. After smiling at Jim, who was still rubbing his eyes, he walked up to Socker and said, "Well, here I am, safe and sound. What about some breakfast?"

To Jim's surprise Socker turned to Kevin and said, "Get out one of the packets of cornflakes and powdered milk. We can use the water now we've got it."

"Preparing for a pretty long siege, are you?" said Jim. "How long do you reckon we'll be together in this house of yours? Month or so?"

Before Socker could answer Willy said, "We've got to get there first. We could be eating this anywhere from here to there."

It was a reasonable enough guess, but it seemed to infuriate Socker, for he shouted, "I've had about enough of you! You can keep your mouth shut from now on, or I'll shut it for you."

Out of the habit of a lifetime Jim braced himself, but again it was not necessary. He saw Willy laugh and settle himself comfortably by the creek to wait for his breakfast.

All that day they scrambled on. The road was no better, but it was no worse, either, and without the wind there was no longer the feeling of being held back — of being deliberately hindered. Tempers were calmer, and the day passed more quickly and more pleasantly. They were high up on a rugged plateau now, and could see the ocean of tree-clad hills rolling away on all sides and, to the south, downwards to the river. Far beyond, on the other side of the river the cleared country was now visible. But it was still miles and miles away, remote, unapproachable, as if it were another world. Their world was here, among these hills and these trees, under this empty sky.

It was when they stopped for lunch where a clump of black wattles made a shade that Jim saw clearly a change was coming over the party. In the preceding two days relationships had subtly altered from the pairing of two dominant and two subservient to one interlocking unit. There was a pecking order still, but it seemed different and, more intriguing as Jim began to understand it, still fluid. It had become noticeable when the early sense of strain had gone. Today they were at peace, and they could almost have been called friends. When he tried to work it out he thought it had something to do with the tree across the road on that first night. They were all cut off together and it was nobody's fault. It was a fact that bound them. The ordeal of the day before had had something to do with it, too. It was again something they had all gone through — something nobody could help. And they all felt a weight lifted when this day had broken calm and kind.

The midday stop was almost cheerful. Socker permitted the opening of a tin of baked beans, and Kevin even produced plastic plates to eat them from. They had saved some water from the creek and no one complained when Kevin asked if he could light a fire and make some tea. There was still no wind and the smoke went straight up and floated off between the branches of the wattles. They sat round the fire, peaceful in the shade, and ·atched the small flames and the crackling twigs and the glowing coals. And when they had eaten their beans they put down their plates and sighed, and looked without rancour at the faces on the other side of the flames. It was a situation that anyone living ten thousand years before would have found familiar. It was the basic situation of men. If Jim did not think quite in these terms he was aware of something binding the four of them. It had nothing to do with the past or the future. It was to do with now, and it was to do with .themselves among these self-sufficient hills — alone.

"Tell us," said Socker in a voice he had not used before. "Tell us about your mum and dad."

The spell was broken. At once Jim was on the defensive. "Why should I?" he said. "You mind your own business."

To his surprise Socker answered mildly, "OK, if you don't want to. I just wondered."

"See, he never had any. Not what you'd call a family, did you, Sock?"

But Kevin was not there to provide sympathy and Socker said, "You keep out of it, Kev. I wasn't talking to you." Even now his tone was milder than usual.

Jim found himself saying, "Anyway, there's nothing to tell. Mum and Dad are just ordinary — like other parents." As soon as he had said it he knew it was not true. Sometimes he had considered the parents of other boys he knew, and he had felt sorry for them because their mothers were just women. Their fathers just men. They could not really be said to have mothers. They did not know what it was to have real fathers. It was a conclusion he had come to long ago, and scarcely ever thought about now. But it came into his mind with Socker's question, and it was something he knew that he would never tell Socker. He could not explain it to Socker if he tried.

"If you never had any family," said Willy, "where do you belong?"

"What do you mean — belong?" Socker looked really puzzled.

51

"Well, just — belong. You got to fit in somewhere, haven't you?"

Socker shrugged. "I suppose I belong in the town back there. I live in the same house with my father, if that's what you mean. But I don't belong to him. I never did. I never belonged to anyone. I never needed to." The note of arrogance was in his voice again.

It had no effect on Willy, who went on, "I don't mean that. I mean what sort of a hole do you leave when you go? Like now. See, there'll be a kind of hole left down there in the town for Jim and me — the place where we fit. You got to have a place too, somewhere. Everyone has."

Jim had never heard Willy talk like this before. But it did not surprise him. Willy never said the sort of things you'd expect. Sometimes, even, he just never said things. He could see what Willy was getting at and he looked closely at Socker to see if he could, too. Perhaps he had, for all at once he changed the subject. He looked at Willy with a kind of smile and said, "You're one of the funniest people I ever met. What made you so funny?"

"He's not funny," said Jim at once. "No funnier than you, anyway."

"I've never been funny at all," said Socker, unruffled. "Nothing funny ever happened in my life. Nothing very good ever happened in my life, if it comes to that — only when I made it happen." He seemed to think of something, for he looked at Willy again. "How do you know this house we're going to, anyway? You been there?"

Willy nodded, his eyes suddenly far away. "A few times."

"How'd you get there? It's miles. You wouldn't have a licence."

Again Jim thought of the times when Willy had been

gone for two or three nights. He had always been allowed to go, for it had seemed that these disappearances were necessary to Willy, and their father had always refused to let him be too carefully looked after. But he never really told them where his rides had taken him. This was where he'd been.

Willy did not seem disposed to answer any more questions, and he only said, "I got a bike," and got up and wandered away from the fire. He walked into the middle of the road and stood looking over the hills, letting the wind blow the hair from his face, oblivious for the moment of the three still sitting round the fire behind him.

It had died down and the tea was cold. Socker got up. "Come on," he said. "It's time to go."

Kevin picked up the billy and would have tossed out the remains of the tea if Jim had not snatched it from him and poured it over the fire. On top of the hissing coals he kicked earth and stamped it down and then kicked more earth on top of that. He knew the fire was out, but he found himself wanting to hide the place where it had been.

During the afternoon they began to go downhill. They no longer saw the distant hilltops or the cleared plains to the south. Bigger trees grew round them and the road became a tunnel, still with its rough, neglected surface, but passable. Theirs were the only wheel tracks on the gravel, theirs the only dust to be blown up and to settle again on the leaves and branches of the roadside shrubs. Ahead of them the road was clear, unmarked, and the overhanging leaves still glistened as the last rain had left them. There was no sign on this side of the ranges of the high wind that had caused them so much trouble on the northern side.

53

CHAPTER

6

IT WAS NIGHT before they reached the house, and Socker had put his lights on. His confidence had returned. He was even cheerful, and he had no doubt that his scheme was going to work. He recognized the road and he knew just when he could expect to see the house. He knew round which narrow bend he would find the track that led to it. They bumped over it, went through a narrow gateway with the wooden gate lying collapsed beside the post to which it was still attached and began to climb steeply up a rough track. After perhaps a quarter of a mile they passed what seemed, in the flash of headlights, to be a few gnarled,

54

half-dead fruit trees and the untidy clump of an old rose bush, and the house loomed up in front of them. It was long and rambling, with a veranda all the way along the front. The track led round the side, and Socker steered the car to the back, where there was a kind of courtyard between the house and some tumbledown sheds.

"Thank God," said Socker, and turned the engine and the headlights off.

In the moment before the car doors were opened Jim was aware of an enveloping blackness and in the corner of his eye, a small, brief streak of light. Before he could be sure he had even seen it, it had gone. Kevin opened his door and the light inside the car came on.

"Out," said Socker. "Quick. And into the house." His voice was harsh, domineering and aggressive. The Socker who had picked them up and who had knocked Kevin on to the hood instead of Willy, was back again.

One after another they climbed out, and the scented, cool night air enveloped them. Jim shivered and looked up at the house. There was not much to see in the darkness, but his eyes were slowly adjusting and he was able to pick out a flight of wooden steps on to a back veranda. The rail had gone, but the steps looked solid. Willy was just ahead of him, following Kevin. He walked up the steps with confidence, either as if he knew them well, or as if he were having no trouble to see in the dark. Jim heard Kevin's step on the veranda boards, then fumbling at what must have been a door.

Then Kevin's voice: "Bring a light, Sock. I can't see anything."

There was a silence, as if Socker were standing very still. Then he said, "We haven't got any lights. You never thought of it, did you?"

"You never told me," said Kevin quickly, and then

55

added, "What about a flashlight? You got a flashlight, haven't you?"

"No," said Socker out of the darkness.

Everyone had stopped moving. Jim found it possible now to see the dim shape of the car just below him, the sheds, a blacker mass, on the far side, and, above, the luminous emptiness of the night sky. The stars were there again, silent and aloof, moving obediently in their courses, shining bright. But they did not light up the veranda.

Kevin fumbled again. There was a scraping, and a small sudden flame. While the match lasted they saw him silhouetted against the door. Then there was a click, the light was extinguished and he disappeared. Jim moved quickly inside as Socker came up the steps behind him.

"Go on," said Socker just beside his ear. "Get in." And he felt a fist in his back.

He did not like being pushed, and he said, "All right. What's the hurry? We're here, aren't we?"

The door behind them banged. The blackness round them was almost tangible. And it smelt. It smelt very strongly of — of—

"Just like a zoo," said Kevin. "Erk!"

"It's only rats. What do you expect?" Socker's voice had become edgy. Jim thought the mistake of forgetting the lights had shown him a weakness he did not care to see. They were all to suffer in consequence. "Here," he said now. "You go back and get the ropes, Kevin. We'll tie them up again."

They were all blundering about in the blackness, half stifling in the strange smell, not knowing when the ceiling might give way above them or their foot might go through a floorboard. All except Willy. Jim suddenly realized that nothing had been seen or heard of Willy since they had all come through the door. Kevin was brushing past him, grumbling. He might as well show that he was present, so he said, "What do you want to tie us up for? Where do you think we're going, anyway?"

"If I can't see you I'm going to be darned sure I know where you are." He had known Socker was still close beside him. Even in the dark, one was aware of Socker's body.

Outside there came a series of crashes, a yelp and a curse. "Your friend has fallen down the steps," said Jim, who did not like being bullied. "Hadn't you better go and help him?"

He suddenly felt a sharp pain by his ear, and his neck clicked as Socker's fist, aimed blindly in the dark, connected with his head. He rubbed his ear and, feeling he had been standing close to Socker long enough, stepped quickly and quietly to one side. He could follow Willy's example and simply disappear. He began creeping forward, feeling for the walls. But a board creaked and Socker was on him and had him painfully by the arm, dragging him back to the middle of the room.

"No you don't," said Socker. And then, it seemed, Kevin was back, for there were more thumps on the steps, a footfall on the veranda and then a voice at the door.

"Here, where are you, Socker?"

"Over here. Bring them to me." And Jim felt his other arm grasped and both were pulled behind him. There was a further fumbling and the rope went round his wrists. Socker was tying it, and it was tight and rather painful, and the knot slid smoothly into place.

"That's fixed you," he heard Socker say. "Now you.

Willy." There was silence. He could hear Socker breathing beside him. "Willy!" Socker's voice, suddenly raised, made him jump. There was still no movement, and he cautiously stepped backward until he could feel the wall behind him. He had a feeling that if Willy could not be found it would be he who would get hit. And his head still hummed from the last blow. Socker had begun charging about in the darkness. His feet clumped on the floor. He was on the far side of the room, and he must have flung a door open, for a faint rectangle of light showed in the darkness.

"You stay by that door, Kevin," Socker shouted, and the rectangle was momentarily blocked as he went through. Jim waited, propped against the wall, and he knew that Kevin was standing unwillingly by the back door. He could hear him breathing, short and uneven, and knew from the smell of him that he was sweating.

Socker's steps could be heard in more distant parts of the house now, sometimes stumbling, sometimes tripping, as he blundered his way about the empty rooms. Jim stayed very quiet, partly in order to upset Kevin rather more, if possible, than he already was, and partly so that he, too, could hear if there was any sign of Willy. He hoped that Willy would not be caught, for it would be more than a slight blow on the side of the head if Socker found him now. Socker was becoming more angry all the time and Socker angry was something to be avoided if possible.

In the end the footsteps returned, the rectangle was again blotted out, and Jim knew Socker was back with them again.

"He's gone," said Socker. "Where's the other? Kevin, where's the other?" His voice was sharp and hard.

Jim let them find him. He knew it would be rough

when they did, but he thought the pleasure of hearing them search would be worth it. In the end it was, but only just, and he was fairly stiff and sore when they had finished dealing with him.

It was after that Kevin made his contribution. "Sock," he suddenly shouted in the darkness. "What about the car? Did you go and leave the keys in it?" Immediately he wished he had not made it, for Socker sent him out a second time.

"And I don't care if you fall down the steps," said Socker as he went. "But hurry. Go on." And Jim heard him tramping off across the veranda, muttering to himself as he went.

Willy was not in the car, and Jim had never thought he would be. Kevin returned with the keys and, without being told, felt for Socker's hand and put them in it.

"Anyway, he won't get far now," said Socker. "I reckon he'll come back to his brother, and while we've got him we're OK."

Jim was not so sure. Just now Willy was unpredictable, and he could not help Jim by staying. On the whole, Jim was glad he had gone, for whatever reason. If nothing else, it provided a confusion in the plans.

To make sure they still did have him, Socker began fumbling at the knots that secured his arms and then, satisfied that he would find Jim in the same place when morning came, told them he was going to sleep by the veranda door.

"Where are you, Kev?" he.said, and Jim heard a gasp as feeling hands made contact. "Right. You go over there, by the hall door, and don't let anyone through in the night." There came a scuffling of footsteps over the floor boards, one or two grunts and sighs from Kevin, and then the sound of bodies settling themselves in comfortable positions.

As nights go, it was an uncomfortable night, and Jim was relieved beyond measure when the first faint gleam of light came through the cracked and cobwebbed windowpanes. He was stiff and cold, and he did not think he had slept at all. He had decided more than once that the sun was never going to rise again. As the light increased he looked round the room. It was bigger than he had thought, stretching the length of the back veranda as far as he could see. To his surprise there was a door in the wall he leant against, not far away. If he had known he might have slipped through before they tied him. This must have been the way Willy had gone. He wondered more than once what Willy was up to. To walk the whole way back was not possible without water, and the way ahead, from what he had seen of it, looked more difficult still. But Willy knew the country. He gave up trying to guess.

Against the door into the front of the house Kevin was sleeping on his back, his mouth open. One hand was flung out across the floor. His face could scarcely have been paler, more waxen, if he had been dead. Even his breathing was so faint, so shallow it was almost imperceptible. Socker was by the back door. He was lying neatly in the doorway on his side, the dark hair half over his face. One hand was under his head, cushioning it on the boards. The other was beside him curved in sleep, half open, but ready for action if it should be needed. He could, even now, grasp an ankle in a split second if one tried to step over him and go through the door. It pleased Jim to think that there was an unguarded door close beside him.

For a few minutes he considered whether it would be

worth creeping away while they slept and now it was light enough to see. He came to the conclusion that with his hands tied and unless there was a chance of finding Willy he would not get far. This time he did not think it was worth the retribution that would inevitably follow. He moved into a more comfortable position and unexpectedly, now that the day was coming, felt very sleepy. There was no reason to struggle to stay awake. There was nothing to be gained. His muscles and his nerves relaxed at last and he allowed himself to fall into sleep.

When he opened his eyes again it was to find the room full of movement and light. Through the murky back windows the sunlight was pouring in, falling in bright splashes on the disturbed dust on the floor. Socker and Kevin were awake and on their feet, and just beside them Willy was standing.

"We knew you wouldn't get far," Socker was saying. "We weren't worrying."

"That's right," came Kevin's faithful echo. "And we got your brother OK."

Willy now looked down at where Jim was lying at his feet. "What about untying him," he said, "now you got us both so safe?"

Jim got up. He half thought Socker would refuse, just out of bloody-mindedness, but he must have got control of himself while he slept, for he jerked his head in Jim's direction and said, "Untie him, Kev. He'll have to be untied for breakfast, anyway."

As he moved, stretching himself and rubbing his wrists, Jim was looking at Willy. There was nothing about him to indicate what he had done or where he had been last night. He looked neither tired nor dishevelled. He looked as if he had just woken from a restful night's sleep. Even his hair — Jim looked once more at his brother's head. Caught in the thicker layers of hair just behind the ear was a piece of bark. It was quite a small piece, but it was the kind of thin, paperlike bark that comes off the trunk of a tall tree — the sort of tree that grows in gullies and damp places, quite a long way from where they were.

Breakfast was of cornflakes and powdered milk and water from a rusty old tank that still stood on a frame at one end of the house. The water tasted reasonably sweet. All through breakfast Socker showed a mounting excitement. He ate more and more quickly, fidgeting as he ate.

At some risk to his personal safety Jim said, "Got a train to catch, Socker?"

This time Socker proved invulnerable. He was not to be pricked. "Kind of," he said amiably. "I've got to talk to your dad, haven't I?"

There was silence for a moment. Jim had forgotten the purpose of their presence here and the shock of remembering was sudden and sharp. But in a little while he said, "You've got a pretty long way to go to the nearest telephone, haven't you?"

"Not so long." Socker was smiling at him now, but not, Jim thought, with affection. "Remember I told you I knew where I could ring up? You don't have to worry. I got it all worked out."

"That's right," said Kevin dutifully.

"What about the river? You've got to cross the river, haven't you? And it's miles away. We saw it from the road yesterday." All at once Jim did not want anything to stand in the way of communication with his father.

To his relief Socker said, "I know a place where I can cross, see? Not where the road goes. Nearer, where the cliffs are. Maybe Willy knows. He knows it all so well."

He clearly did not expect Willy to know, and this was why he said it. But Willy, who had been looking out of the window and had not seemed to be listening, looked at Socker now and said quietly, "You won't be able to cross the river."

Socker laughed. "You don't know it. And I thought you knew everything. I can cross it. I've crossed it before."

"Not today. You won't be able to cross it today." Willy bent his head and went on with his cornflakes.

For a moment Socker's face went blank. The black brows came down and he looked at Willy from beneath them. Then he threw back his head and laughed. "You can't fool me. You can't pull that trick twice." He pushed the plate away from him and stood up on the veranda step. Kevin, halfway through a mountainous plateful, jumped up too. He was full of eagerness, even relief.

"What do you think you're doing?" said Socker.

"I'm coming," said Kevin. "I'm coming with you. I don't mind me cornflakes."

Socker looked at him. "Sit down. You're not coming."

"Why not? You said — I don't want —" His eyes began to roll.

"Sit down," Socker shouted at him.

Slowly Kevin subsided, the eagerness draining from his face and dismay taking its place. "Why?" he said almost in a whisper.

"Use your head, if you can. Think we can leave these two on their own here? Think we'd find them when we got back?"

"Where'd they go? There's nowhere, Sock. They'd have to stay." He looked over his shoulder at Jim and Willy as if they were caged beasts. "Anyway, see, Sock, they'd be two to one."

"What do you think I brought you for? Think I'd divide up the money with you if I didn't need you? You've got the gun, haven't you? Tie them up again if you're so scared. You stay here. And you better be here when I get back."

Kevin was on his feet again. "Don't go, Sock. Don't go. Help me tie them first."

"Go and get the ropes." Socker's face was not at all pretty, and Jim did not care to have it thrust into his own, nor to feel his arm grabbed by the elbow so that he was dragged to his feet. The plastic spoon dropped out of his hand. Out of the corner of his eye he saw Willy quickly gobbling the last of his cornflakes. Then he got to his feet too. Willy never did like to be touched.

Socker wasted no time, but once again the knots he tied were going to stay tied. As he jumped down the two bottom steps and made for the car he shouted, "Better come and get the gun." Almost before Kevin was off the veranda he had opened the door, snatched the rifle and thrown it. With a gasp Kevin caught it, and was just in time to catch the packet of bullets that followed it. Then Socker was in the car, the door banged and the engine exploded into action. He rammed in the gear, bounded forward with a scatter of gravel, turned, and was gone down the track, round the corner of the house and out of sight. They could hear him going down the hill, heard the squeak of brakes as he came to the gateway and then the fading sound of the engine as he made off down the road — down to his secret place on the river that Willy said he could not cross.

7

THE DUST WAS SETTLING in the yard, the startled birds were tuning up again and the smell of carbon monoxide began to float into their nostrils. Kevin walked up the steps carrying the rifle. "You can sit down," he said, and there was a nervous bluster in his voice.

"We'll sit down while you finish your breakfast," said Jim amiably. He was learning about Kevin.

They all sat down and Jim talked kindly to Kevin while he finished his cornflakes. He spoke of pleasant things like football games and gangster films and how outstanding Kevin must be to have been chosen by

Socker as the one to help him, and how likely it was that at such a time Socker would be nervy and snap back at Kevin when he had suggested something quite reasonable. As if there was any escape from here. What an idea, and who would want to, anyway, into a parched and waterless bush with no other shelter than this house for miles. Willy, beside him, nodded and dreamed and looked so helpless and vague that before very long Kevin had untied their hands, feeling much happier and much safer. Alone in a place like this Kevin had to have the humans on his side or he was lost. It made him feel much more comfortable when Jim and Willy were able to walk about and do things like him, and were able to stand, somehow, between him and all that outdoors beyond the house.

For a time Jim worked hard on Kevin. He knew Kevin was a leaner, and all he had to do was to provide a prop. When he was satisfied that Kevin was leaning, he decided to explore the house. It was not difficult, having suggested that Kevin should lead the way, to go as he wanted to. Willy walked beside him, saying nothing, and Kevin followed because he did not want to be first and he did not want to be left alone.

The house certainly smelt like a zoo. Each room seemed to smell worse than the last. Here and there were even little tufts of parti-coloured fur. "What is it?" said Jim at last. "It doesn't look like possums."

"Cats, I expect," said Willy.

"Funny we don't see them then. They can't have been gone too long by the smell." Jim was looking in the dark corners of the floor.

"Oh, you won't see them," said Willy.

The house was mainly of weatherboard, here and there patched up with sheets of corrugated iron where the boards had rotted or fallen away. They found that there were small rooms on either end of the back veranda. The one on the left had clearly been a bedroom, for the sagging frame of an iron bedstead remained in one corner. There had once been a hair mattress on it, but a succession of animals seemed to have made nests in the mattress and it was now no more than twisted heaps of horsehair held together in places by torn and stained pieces of ticking. The smell was worst of all here and they backed out swiftly. On the other end of the veranda remained what was left of the laundry and, perhaps, bathroom, for here and there a pipe leaned drunkenly outward from the wall with a tap, once over a basin or tub, now waving aimlessly as the pipe swung from its broken fitting, searching, it seemed, for somewhere to discharge its load of water. Jim took one in his hands and turned the tap. To his surprise it disgorged a clotted dark brown flow of water on to the floor. He turned it off quickly. "Must still be hitched to that old tank," he said. The tubs, or basins, or whatever had furnished it once, had all disappeared, perhaps through the floor, for there were places where the boards gaped into an unfathomable blackness beneath. From the blackness rose a dusty, feral smell. Going through the kitchen door to the front of the house they came into a hall and faced the front door. Once the top half of it had been filled in with stained glass — an imposing entrance so far from anywhere. But with the passing of time the lead had weakened and most of the pieces of glass had fallen out. Many still lay about the hall. Through the gaping space left by the glass they could see the front veranda that Jim had briefly glimpsed as they approached the night before. It was in much worse repair than the back veranda. Most of the boards had rotted at the end and several veranda posts had broken, so that the sheets of iron above hung in the wind, creaking and moaning, waiting only for one strong blow to set them free and send them down the hill. The front steps, however, remained intact, for they were of stone. They still stood, wide, impressive and inviting, with a low stone balustrade on either side.

The sitting room was a long room to the left of the hall. It went the whole length of the house, and one could see through the window frame at the far end to the blue-grey hills in the distance. It gaped open to the weather, for the window had fallen out. The walls bore the remains of a patterned wallpaper, once of startling design and shade but faded now to a uniform biscuit colour. In the middle of the room where, perhaps, there had once been a chandelier, the ceiling had come down and a well-scuffled-through pile of plaster and splinters of wood had spread over a large part of the floor. Through the hole in the ceiling it was possible to see some of the roofing beams and the underside of the roofing iron. In the far corner the floor, too, had given way and a draught came up through the hole. Two rooms on the right side of the house, one leading off the front hall and the other from the kitchen, had no doubt been bedrooms, but the outside wall had gone, blown down, clawed down, it almost looked like, and open to the weather. The floorboards, though still in position, looked unsafe and served only to conceal what lay beneath them. In all the rooms stained and once damp patches on the floor and ceilings showed where the roof leaked. The only brickwork in the place was the chimney from the kitchen range, now a rusting heap of iron, which backed on to the sitting room fireplace. This still stood strong and firm and remained, now that

68

everything else was crumbling round it, the kingpin of the house.

"Fancy your knowing about this old place," Jim said to Willy as they came out again onto the back veranda.

"It's somewhere to come in the rain," said Willy, and ran down the steps to the courtyard.

"Hey, where are you going?" said Kevin.

"Just having a look at the weather. Coming?" said Willy. Jim was already beside him. Kevin, looking as if he were descending into a rough and possibly cold sea, came down after them.

On the other side of the yard there once had been a toolshed, a garage or stable and a hen house, but, having been made more carelessly, they were in even worse repair than the house. Beyond them the hill continued up for quite some distance and trees grew thickly to its crest. Tangled wires and drunken posts still surrounded the house and sheds, and at the front enclosed quite a large slice of the hillside. Whoever had come to settle here had come with big ideas. Why they had come, and even more, why, having put so much work and money into the place, they had gone again was not at all obvious. There was no sign that a bush fire had driven them out. Jim came to the conclusion they had found it too lonely. It was far too lonely for him. As for Kevin, there was no doubt now who was looking after whom. If they wanted to get away now they would be taking Kevin with them.

But, as Jim looked about at the armies of trees that surrounded the house and cleared ground, creeping closer with every passing season, it was hard to say what they would be escaping to. Escaping from the house was one thing, but the house itself seemed to offer escape from the wilderness that encroached on all sides. Somehow Socker and his demand for ransom no longer seemed important. There were bigger issues at stake, and these would affect all of them. Jim wished very much that he was safely back among the things he knew.

The day passed slowly. The heat increased, and by midday the bush surrounding them had fallen silent. Only the old house, baking beneath the sun, seemed to groan among its splitting timbers. Now and then the roofing iron cracked like a rifle shot in the hills, making them all jump. Kevin was alternately suspicious and overfriendly. Once or twice he reached for the rifle and, at last, having watched him draw back the bolt and ram the bullet in with twitchy fingers, Jim said, "Who are you going to shoot, Kev?"

"I don't know yet, do I? But I'll be ready if I have to." There were tiny glistening drops on his forehead.

It might be safer for them all if Kevin could be separated from the rifle, but this would require thought and planning. Jim glanced at Willy, sitting beside him on the edge of the veranda. Willy, as usual, had been very quiet all day. Jim wanted badly to talk, but there had not been an opportunity.

It came after what should have been lunch. Nobody had thought to unload the car before Socker went off with it, and now there was no food. Kevin seemed to be expecting him back at any moment. Willy appeared resigned to the present state of affairs and sat quietly, looking always into the trees beyond. Jim half believing Willy, half hopeful with Kevin, sat swinging his legs listening for the sound of the returning car. Presently, hearing a small sound from Kevin's direction he looked over his shoulder. Kevin was sitting with his head back against the kitchen wall. His mouth was open and his eyes were closed. Kevin had begun to snore. Jim turned to Willy and raised his eyebrows. Willy nodded, and slowly, cautiously, they got up, crept down the steps, slipped along under the shelter of the veranda boards, and round the corner of the house. Here they stopped. There was no sound except, very faintly, Kevin's snores. Willy took Jim by the sleeve and led him off towards the trees. They crossed the open, tussocky ground and came to the tangled remains of the fence. Stepping over the fallen wires they pushed their way through a grove of spindly saplings and were in among the tall trunks. To be in the shade was a relief. Willy led the way to a fallen log conveniently placed so that they could watch the house. They sat down, side by side, and at last Jim said what he had been wanting to say for so long.

"Willy, what's going to happen? What'll we do?"

It was a little time before Willy spoke. He was not as sure of the answer as Jim had hoped. At last he said, "I don't think that Socker'll get over the river. He thinks I don't know the place, but I do. There's just one place where you can jump if the water's low. I don't know. It could have rained since he was there. He's not going to get over."

Finding that Willy had no more to say, Jim asked, "What happens then? We're all stuck here? Can we get out?"

Willy shook his head. "You and me, I think we could. But not with those two in the car behind us. We'd never get through. It's a long way. If we got to where the tree fell we could make it from there. But, see, we'd have to carry water, and we'd have to stick to the road most of the way to get that far, and they'd have the car to catch us."

Jim sighed and kicked his heels against the log. On the ground below, a small black ant was dragging the head and one attached wing of a blowfly over some wiry grass. The wing, like a sail catching contrary winds, kept sticking on the blades of grass. The ant kept having to let go and take a new grip, pulling first this way and then that. Painstakingly it got the remains of the fly to within six inches of the log and then they jammed properly. No amount of pulling and tugging, of changing position and jawhold made any difference. It had them stuck in what must have been the main highway for home, because another ant now came hurrying along, bumping into the first as it tugged away backwards. Jim watched some incomprehensible maneuvering between them and then saw the second ant take hold of the wing. They both pulled and the head began to move. It slid out from the tussock where it was jammed and moved off smoothly down the beaten path, pulled by both ants. When all had disappeared beneath the log Jim lifted his head.

"If we could," he said. "If only we could get there first, while they're still stuck with the car, we could bring people back to catch them."

"Do you think they'd believe us?" said Willy. "If we said we'd been kidnapped, and then Socker said we hadn't, do you think they'd believe *us?* Socker's older and able to drive a car and all. If he said they never, why would anyone believe us?"

"Well, they would," said Jim, suddenly angry at the idea that after all they'd been through it could be Socker and not they who would be believed. But when it came to dealing with people he was more sanguine than Willy. He sat up and looked Willy in the eye. "They would believe us. They'd have to. Why would we want to come to a place like this, with coves like that? We never did before." And then he remembered that Willy often did it. It was what Willy liked to do best of all. He felt a sudden misgiving.

But Willy only said, "We'd never do it — honest, Jim.

72

We could do it the other way, across the river, where Socker was going, if we could get across the river. But not back the way we came. See, we'd need the water, and even now it's a while since we've eaten. We'd start empty."

"If we waited till Socker got back. There's water in the tank and there's food in the car. We could sneak off when they weren't looking, like we have now."

"Do you think we'd sneak away from Socker that easy? Someone like Socker would use the rifle. He'd shoot at us while we were getting as far as the trees."

"He'd never hit us. Not if we ran fast." Jim was full of enthusiasm now. Getting away no longer seemed impossible, and he could not really believe anyone — even Socker — would actually shoot him.

"I'd be afraid, Jim. I couldn't do it." Willy was pleading, begging to be let off. Yet he had slipped away for the whole of the night before, just because he had not fancied being in the house with Socker and Kevin. But this was the Willy Jim knew, and somewhere there was a difference. It was no good persuading. If Willy could not, he could not.

"Very well, if you don't think we'd make it." Once again Jim felt the heavy weight of responsibility. In this unfriendly wilderness it was all the harder.

But suddenly Willy smiled, and Willy's smile was always heartening. That pale, lugubrious face broke into a thousand creases. The dreamy eyes vanished, twinkling through a pucker of eyebrows and screwed-up lids. One had to smile when Willy smiled. He put his arm across Jim's shoulders and said, "It'll be all right. In the end it'll be all right, Jim. If the worst comes to the worst I know a place . . ." He stopped, and then said, "So long as we don't try and be smart with that Socker. Socker will find out — see, there's . . ." Jim waited, but he had decided not to go on.

Before Jim could press him there came in the afternoon stillness the sound of a shot. They heard Kevin's voice shouting. Then they saw Kevin run round the side of the house waving the rifle. He stopped and fired again at random, and somewhere among the treetops the bullet whistled. Jim pulled Willy off the log and they crouched beside it. "Silly beggar," he said. "He's not even aiming at anything. He'll end by shooting us all if we're not careful. What does he think he's doing?"

"He's panicking," said Willy. "We'll have to wait till he's calmed down." He looked round him in a strange way and added, "He'll frighten everything, going on this way."

It seemed to Jim a funny thing to worry about, but it was true that the shots had silenced the birds. There was no sound at all now Kevin was silent.

He called out a few more times, but at the final frenzied shout his voice cracked, and after that he did not call again. They waited for a long time in the hot afternoon, wiping flies from their faces and ants from various parts of their bodies. Then, eventually they crept back. Jim drew a long breath as they reached the cover of the house and no shots had been fired. He was about to step round the corner when he felt Willy's hand on his arm, and found himself drawn in through the broken wall of the end bedroom and down beneath the floorboards. Bent double, with Willy's hand still holding his, he crept through the odorous and unpleasant darkness. Willy seemed to know exactly where he was going and only paused once, when Jim heard the high, faint sound of mewing. Willy had been right about the

74

cats. After the sound, Willy took him in a semi-circle and Jim thought how strange it was at such a time to be so careful to avoid frightening a kitten. Then the darkness lessened, and they came to the hole in the corner of the living room floor. Willy looked through it, and finding the room empty as he had expected, he crawled through, and Jim crawled through after him.

It was hard to avoid squeaking boards and it was hard to open doors without making any noise, but they managed to do so and reached the kitchen at last. Through the open door leading to the back veranda they could see Kevin. He had returned to the safety of the house and was standing at the top of the steps looking in all directions. The rifle was leaning against the kitchen door. Quietly Willy crossed the kitchen, took hold of the rifle and handed it to Jim. Then they walked out to Kevin.

Hearing the footsteps behind him, Kevin spun round, making a dive for where he had left the rifle. Finding himself face to face with his charges, seeing the rifle firmly held in Jim's arm, he stopped dead, opened his mouth and made a sound that might have meant anything from joy to terror.

"Here we are," said Jim. "You can relax now."

All afternoon they waited for Socker. Little by little the sun moved lower into the west. Little by little the shadows crept across the courtyard. The searing heat went out of the day. Swallows began to swoop after the first insects of evening, magpies gurgled their relief at the cooling breeze and not far off, in the tops of the trees a family of kookaburras laughed together.

Jim took the bullet out of the rifle, picked up the packet when Kevin was not looking and put it in his pocket and then handed back the rifle. "There you are, Kev," he said. "Now we'll all be safe."

75

Just before dark they wandered down the track to the road, for it was not only Socker they wanted to see now, it was food. Jim and Willy walked together and Kevin walked behind. He did not seem to want to be left by himself in the house, however safe. There were the tracks, scored deep in the sand and gravel of the roadside ditch, that Socker had made when he went out. There were the curving tire marks in the road, where he had spun the car round, accelerating as he did so. They could see where the little shower of pebbles had scattered, fanshaped, on the verge of the road. The tracks were visible all the way down to the next corner. But the road was empty, and there was no sound of an approaching vehicle. Peering at the corner, willing him to come round, it seemed strange to Jim that he should be so eager to see Socker again. But Socker would be bringing news of their parents. By now they would be worrying, and he wondered if they would worry less or more after speaking to Socker. Thinking of the lottery money, so recently won, so soon to be lost, he felt a pang, and wished that Socker would come very quickly to a bad end. But most of all he wished for a return to home and ordinary life.

It was quite dark when they left the road and climbed the track again to the house. No amount of waiting and searching and wishing had brought even the sound of the distant engine, grinding its way up the hill it had earlier gone down so fast. It was Kevin who had wanted to go back, but there had been little point in staying, so they all went.

Walking up the track, with the house looming dark on the hillside, Jim was reminded of their arrival the night before. Then, the house was strange and still unknown. Now, it was as if they had known it for a lifetime.

They turned the corner into the courtyard and, as they did so, something rushed silently across the yard in front of them. In the dark it was impossible to see whether it was large or small, furred, feathered, or scaled. It disappeared into, or under, the house, and Jim found himself letting out his breath in slow relief as he realized it was probably only a cat.

Kevin had stopped dead and now said shrilly, "What was that?"

Willy said nothing. "Only a cat," said Jim.

They had nothing to do but wait. They drank water out of cupped hands or from the plastic plates or spoons. They was nothing else to drink from. And there was still nothing to eat. They all wondered what had happened to delay Socker, but no one made any suggestions. No one cared to speak of it at all. As the night deepened Kevin wanted to go inside, but neither Jim nor Willy were keen to shut themselves away from the night outdoors. So Kevin sat with them on the veranda. They leaned against the wall and gazed out across the courtyard to the shadowy heap of sheds and the deep shade of the trees climbing the hill behind, and the navy blue sky high up beyond the hilltop. Small sounds that they could not place came now and then to their ears, as the nocturnal life of the bush woke and moved and began to hunt for its food. Each blade of grass and pendant leaf gave off fresh and spicy odours that mingled and filled the night with one composite smell — the smell of dry summer nights everywhere.

Still there was no sound of an approaching car, and still Socker did not come. One by one they wriggled, slipped down, settled themselves as comfortably as they could, and drifted into sleep.

CHAPTER

8

I T W A S W I L L Y who heard the footsteps first. Jim felt his shoulder gripped and heard Willy's voice in his ear. "He's here. He's come without the car." He sat up, wide-eyed, and heard the slow crunch of footsteps in the courtyard. They waited until they sensed he had reached the bottom of the steps, then Jim said, "Socker?"

There was a clatter beside him as Kevin woke and began to breathe heavily. A sound of tired feet on the steps, and Socker's voice, beaten, exhausted.

"I couldn't cross the river. I fell in. And I lost the car keys."

78

Neither Jim nor Willy said anything, but after a moment Kevin said, "Then where's the food? Didn't you bring any with you? We haven't had anything to eat all day."

"Shut up," was all Socker said, and then he went inside. "Come on," came his voice through the door. "You'll all come inside with me. Kevin, bring the rifle."

His voice was flat and lifeless, but without a word they all got up and went inside, and Kevin dragged the empty rifle by the barrel. Nobody told Socker it was unloaded, or that the bullets were in Jim's pocket. He shut the door and made them lie down in the kitchen. Jim and Willy lay under the window that opened onto the back veranda. Socker lay with his back to the veranda door and Kevin lay beside the brick chimney and did not see in the dark that a hole had been burnt in the floor at some time by a piece of wood falling out of the fire box. It was late in the night and still without a word they went to sleep again.

They were woken by a scream from Kevin. It was bright daylight and the sun shone in as it had the day before. Jim woke in time to see Kevin writhe upward from the floor, where he seemed to have been lying on his stomach. His left arm must have slipped through the hole in the floor as he slept, for he pulled his hand out as he got up and clutched it, moaning, to his chest. From the doorway Socker watched him out of bloodshot, weary eyes.

It was Jim who said, "What's up? Kevin, what happened?"

When Kevin was able to stop moaning he said in a whisper that threatened to develop into another scream, "I been bitten. Something bit me."

"Let's have a look." Jim got up and went to him. For

a moment Kevin seemed reluctant to release his hand, as if he thought it might come to pieces if he let it go. Then, reluctantly, he allowed Jim to take his forearm and pull it away from his chest. There was blood on the hand now, but at first it was difficult to see where it was coming from. Kevin began to moan again when he saw the blood. Then Jim, who was turning it over slowly, letting the blood drip down onto the floor, said, "That's where it's coming from. See? There's a mark there." He pointed with his right hand. "And there's another." Where he pointed the blood was welling up, dark, almost purple from the bruised flesh.

Kevin bent his head in fascinated horror. Then suddenly his face became chalk white and he began to make little screaming sounds through his nose.

"Now what's the matter?" said Jim, who still had a firm hold of his hand.

"It's a snake bite. That's what it is — a snake bite! See the two holes?" There were, indeed, two holes, and there were two matching holes in the palm. Kevin's hand was not a pretty sight.

Willy, who had been watching with a kind of still concentration, now came over and looked at the hand. Kevin stood, trembling all over. In a moment he would become hysterical. Willy's face was expressionless as he said, "That's not a snake bite. Look how wide those marks are apart. There's no snake as big as that." That there were other marks as well as the two deep holes, which would not have been made by any snake, he could also have said. But he did not. He continued to say only, "It's not a snake bite," till Kevin seemed to take in what he was saying. When the trembling lessened and the colour returned to his face, Willy walked away and stood looking out of the window.

"Give us your handkerchief," said Jim, "and I'll wrap it up." When Kevin predictably failed to produce a handkerchief they tore a piece off the tail of his shirt and bound up the hand as best they could. The bleeding showed no signs of lessening. The holes must have been fairly deep. Jim tucked the hand into the opening of Kevin's shirt and told him to keep it there.

When there was no more to be done for Kevin and he was again sitting, nursing his arm with his back to the wall, Socker said, "If it wasn't a snake, what was it?"

From the window Willy turned to look at him. But he had nothing to say in reply and presently he resumed his study of the morning outside. Jim opened his mouth to speak, but shut it again without having spoken. No cat would have a jaw that big.

Kevin's hand remained painful. He became a liability. There was nothing he could do, it seemed, that did not cause him excruciating pain, and all he wanted was to return to town and be looked after. "Why didn't you bring the food back?" he said when he realized he had other reasons for discomfort than his hand. "We're all starving here."

Socker was on his feet now and they were hurting him. With a great show of forbearance he said, "I thought I told you I lost the keys. Without keys you can't drive a car. Did you think I was going to carry the food back for you? It took me seven hours to get back without the food. You think I love you that much?"

They stayed in the kitchen all morning. Socker was too tired to move and he would not allow the others to go out without him — only singly, when they said they had to. Kevin told him the rifle was not loaded, and he made Jim give him the packet of bullets. It was strange how, inside the house, the pecking order had reverted to

81

what it had originally been. It was Socker and Kevin again, against Jim and Willy. And Socker was talking about his rights again. It was his right, it seemed, to have the rifle and the bullets, in spite of the fact that the rifle, as Jim and Willy now learnt without surprise, belonged to Kevin's father. It was Socker's right, too, to have something to eat, and he blamed Kevin for not thinking of taking the food out of the car before he left.

Jim felt obliged to speak up. "Kevin's not that bright, Socker. But even if he had been, you never gave him a chance. You were in such a hell of a hurry to get to your telephone you didn't even wait till we finished breakfast."

"You shut up," said Socker. "I'll tell you when I want your help."

"OK," said Jim. "But don't expect to get it. You got no rights over me that I know of."

Socker immediately waved the rifle. "This gives me all the right I need. I know what's due to me." He was angry, as he had been all morning, but he seemed too tired to offer any very alarming physical violence.

Jim, banking on his exhaustion, said, "You seem to have spent a lot of time working out what's due to you. Have you worked out who's going to give it to you?"

For a moment Socker looked at him without speaking. His eyes were half closed and there was a bad-tempered twist to his mouth. "Just now I reckon you are. You or your dad. It's a chance to square the record I never had before. I'd be a fool to let a chance like that slip, wouldn't I?"

Inside the four walls Willy remained cowed and silent. But now he spoke. "Your chance has gone, Socker. You know that."

As the day wore on and they became increasingly

82

hungry, it began to seem to them all as if Willy was right. Kevin, with his well-developed instinct for survival, began to talk civilly to Jim.

While the day was bright outside, the mystery of Kevin's damaged hand had not seemed to weigh heavily on Socker, or even on Kevin. But late in the afternoon when the sunlight had gone from the courtyard and the kitchen began to grow dark the question of what it was that lurked beneath the house — what kind of beast or reptile owned the teeth that had sunk themselves into Kevin's flesh — seemed to grow of itself among the dust motes that hung in the still, shadowy air. Kevin moved himself to a farther distance still from the chimney piece, hovering between putting himself beside Socker or beside Jim. In the end he chose Socker but it was clearly a half-hearted choice. Socker himself was becoming uneasy and his eyes moved constantly from one dark corner of the kitchen to another.

Jim noticed their tensing nerves and knew the reason. He was not very happy about it himself, but he had Willy beside him, and Willy had reassuringly retired into himself as his habit was, and showed no concern for what there might be beneath the house. Jim suspected that he knew.

When the last of the light had gone and they again faced the prospect of a long, black night in the house, Kevin's voice came from the corner where he sat. "What about us all going to the car — now. It wouldn't take too long downhill and there'd be food."

Jim held his breath. He was starving, and a pinched ache had been growing in his stomach for some time. If he had thought Socker would have agreed to it, he would long ago have suggested setting off for the car. But Socker was likely to decide against it just because it was Jim's idea. Socker had probably eaten something before he left the car yesterday. Jim was not entirely surprised when Socker said no one was to move out of the kitchen until he said so — and he had not said so yet. But he was surprised when Socker said, "We've got to get to the food, but we'll go in the daylight. I'm not moving out of this house till it's light, and if I don't go, you don't." It sounded, the way he said it, as if his walk back in the dark of the night before had not been pleasant, for more reasons than the punishment to his feet. Jim wondered why. Of all the faults he would have given Socker, cowardice was not one.

They settled down to pass yet another night in the empty house. Empty? Jim thought not. When there is no light except daylight the night is very long indeed. Partly because they were not sleepy, having spent the whole day in the same room, and partly to stave off the time when they would be forced to sleep, they talked more than they had talked before. Only Willy remained silent as usual. It was not as it had been by the campfire. Here Socker was boss and they all knew it. But he was not above communicating and he told them what he thought of various aspects of the life of their community, particularly the social side of it, which was criminally unjust to anyone who had the bad luck to have no money and no standing. This injustice was something that bothered Socker a great deal, and he intended to do something about it. For Kevin too? No, not for Kevin, you fool. For himself. No one had had the bad luck he'd had. He was as good as anyone else, but look what he got. And there they went with their three cars a family and their sarcastic talk. Who? Almost anyone who wasn't Socker. He'd show them.

"That's right, Sock. No one ever got the better of you,

I reckon." Kevin was away on the wings of Socker's eloquence. His voice came sycophantic from the darkness.

"Only one or two when I was a kid. You're at a disadvantage when you're small." A kind of modesty forced the odd statement out of him.

"That's right. Not everyone has a mother like yours was."

"You shut your mouth before I knock your head off." It was said with such virulence that Kevin shrank back. Again the snail, all extended, horns wide and eager, withdrew hurriedly into the shell.

"Sorry, Sock. I only meant you done well considering."

"I don't care what you meant. You shut up."

After that no one spoke. Kevin did not dare. Jim, in amazement, was contemplating the abyss that had been so unexpectedly revealed. Somewhere in the abyss he knew he would find the why of Socker, if he ever felt like going deep enough.

After a time, perhaps to overlay the brief chink in his armour, Socker began to talk again. "At school I never got a fair go. The teachers never liked me because I was one too much for them. Except the football coach. Got on with him OK. Then look at the jobs I had. You mightn't believe it but I never had a boss yet that didn't try to get the better of me. Thought they could put it over when they saw me. I could fix that pretty quick. I got to know my rights, see? You always got to know your rights to get on. So I reckoned one day I'd make them all sit up and take notice, and when you kids started telling the world about your lottery win I said to myself, 'Here's your chance, Sock, old boy.' Too bad we've run into a bit of trouble, but I'm not beat yet. No, sir."

For the first time Willy spoke. "None of us are beat yet, are we?"

Jim wondered what Socker's reply would be, but he made no reply except, "You say some queer things, don't you?" with a kind of wondering respect. Then, at last, he said, "I'm tired. You can all shut up and go to sleep now."

Jim pushed himself a little nearer to Willy and slid down flat on the floor. He'd be better asleep than awake and thinking of his stomach. As he dropped off he felt Willy's hand grip his own. It gave a hard, quick pressure and let go.

During the day Socker had allowed Kevin to bring back from one of his trips outside a piece of corrugated iron, which had been put over the hole in the floor, with four pieces of brick to keep it down. All the doors were shut, and they settled in reasonable confidence. Only the chimney remained unblocked, open to the sky and, although they did not know it, to the sitting room on the other side.

Jim woke slowly some hours later. He had no idea how long he had been asleep. He had no idea whether something had woken him or whether he had woken of his own accord. He was not cold and he was not especially uncomfortable lying on the boards, and he was not alarmed. There was no sound at all from Willy beside him, but over by the door he could hear Socker's heavy, regular breathing. Not far from him came the sound of Kevin's restless sleep. Sighs, uneven breaths, moans and grunts gave away his position.

Jim closed his eyes and prepared to sleep again, when he realized that his third sense was telling him something. He sniffed. Tomcat. Without a doubt, tomcat. He had only half believed Willy but he might have known he would be right about that.

Undisturbed but curious, he opened his eyes again. From where he lay he commanded most of the floor; only Socker and the back door were out of his range of vision. As he continued to stare into the darkness, breathing quietly, his eyes wide open, he found that he was seeing something. Straight in front of him by the ruined range were two small points of greenish light. They were perhaps eighteen inches from the floor and they glowed steadily, as if reflecting the moonlight outside the window. Then, as he watched, they began to move slowly. They moved together, and he knew they were a pair of eyes. Only a cat, he thought, and his breath came unhurried and smooth. There was no sound, but suddenly the twin lights went out. For a few seconds he retained them on his retina and it seemed to him that they were remarkably wide apart for the eyes of a cat.

He began to concentrate on his ears, as his eyes no longer told him anything. Was there the faintest sound of a soft footfall? He could not be sure. Just then Kevin gave a more than usually violent snort and for the moment he heard nothing more. But now he lay wide awake and alert. It hardly seemed necessary to wake anyone else, but he was curious. If it was a cat it must be a wild cat, and he knew the wild cats about the town seldom came any closer to people than they could help. On the other hand perhaps the people who had left so inexplicably had left their cat behind. Perhaps this was a cat that had, ever since, been searching for its people to come back. He did not know how long cats lived, and the house had been empty for a long time. But still. . . . Then he began to wonder if it were a real cat. Did cats, deserted, remain as ghosts? He remembered the smell of tomcat and was reassured. He could not believe a ghostly cat could retain that powerful, pungent smell.

He was still listening, still peering into the darkness when there was a sudden roar from Socker. It seemed to come from the very roots of his vocal cords. Then came the sound of frenzied scrabbling on the floorboards, a kind of scratching as well as the heavier thuds of Socker's shoes and elbows against the door. And Jim's eardrums were almost split a second time by a piercing scream from Kevin. As he jumped up he knew that there was something on the range. Muffled sounds from within the chimney told him where the cat had gone. The kitchen was pandemonium. All four of them were on their feet, and Kevin and Socker seemed to be charging about, shouting simultaneously. Jim felt a hard body bump into him, and he retired to the side of the window and stood with the wall against his back. Enough light was coming through the window to show its position. All that would be visible in the kitchen would be what was silhouetted against it. He saw the outline of Willy's head, fleetingly, and then felt Willy beside him.

"What was it?" he whispered. He had no doubt that Willy would know.

"Only the cats. I told you," Willy whispered back. "But, Jim, they're not like ordinary cats. They're such big cats." He said no more and Jim immediately forgot what he said because Socker had begun a more articulate shouting.

"Put that down, Kevin. Put that down, I say. You damned fool, what's the good of a gun in the dark?"

There came a clatter, and presumably Socker had snatched the rifle from Kevin and thrown it to the floor.

It said something for his self-control that he did not hold onto it himself.

The sounds of confusion began to lessen. Socker and Kevin stopped moving about and the sounds they uttered began to make sense. Jim listened to what Socker was saying. "Kevin, was that you? Did you come over to me when I was asleep? What were you trying to do? Someone was breathing in my face. I could see his eyes right up against mine. Was it you, Jim? Willy, where are you?"

Before either of them had time to reply Kevin began to shout. "It wasn't me. It was a big furry thing and it smelt. It clawed all over my face." On the word, "face" his voice rose to a shriek, as if the memory were too horrible to be borne. He went on, "I felt it on top of me — hot, all furry and *heavy*. It's the thing that bit my hand. It's in the room somewhere. It's still in here with us. That's why I wanted the gun." He ended on a kind of sob.

Socker had suddenly become very still. Then, when Kevin had finished he said slowly, "Everybody go and stand by the window."

"Willy and I are by the window," said Jim. He knew they would be safer, whatever happened, if Socker knew where they were. Kevin, from wherever he had been, made a rush across the floor. His sweating, trembling body cannoned into Jim. "Now we're all here," said Jim when he had got his breath back. "We're on the far side of the window from you, all together."

"OK, then. Stay there," said Socker, and Jim heard him pick up the rifle. He began to walk softly round the kitchen. They heard his footsteps, muffled but heavy. He was walking, for all his sore feet, on tiptoe. Jim knew, and Jim knew that Willy knew, he would discover nothing, but he had to find out for himself. It was not pleasant to have Kevin pressing so close against him. Kevin twitched and smelt too much.

They heard Socker return to the back door. "There's nothing there," he said. "We must have dreamed it. If there'd been something I couldn't help but find it. There's nothing there."

Pressed against Jim, Kevin's body seemed to vibrate. "You wait till you see me face. You wait till it's light and you see me face. There was something there all right. You wait till you see what it did to me."

"Then where is it now?" said Socker. "I tell you there's nothing there." For the first time his own voice was strained.

Kevin began to whine, "I want to go outside. I don't want to stay in here any longer. Let's go outside, Sock."

Socker seemed to hesitate. The insensitive determination that was his strength began to desert him. He opened the door. "OK," he said at last. "We'll all go on the veranda. We'll wait there till day comes." He stood beside the door while they filed past him, counting and feeling with his big hands as they went through the doorway. Jim was not sorry to be out of the kitchen prison and away from that all-pervading smell. It was odd no one else had noticed it. But Willy would have, and would not have said anything. He was breathing deeply as he stepped out, collecting lungsful of the night air. Jim knew that in a way he was replenishing himself. All that time in the kitchen had reduced Willy, had drained his vitality, had shrivelled him. Now the vitality was pouring back. He was opening out, expanding, growing, fitting himself happily into the linking strands of all the open, teeming land about him. He was settling into the hole he had left. He was tuning in again.

Socker made them sit with their backs to the wall along the veranda. He sat at the end, and Jim thought the rifle was across his knees. No one slept again that night. They sat facing the east and when the first faint glow of daylight began to distinguish the hilltop from the sky, Socker put down the rifle and stood up. "The night's over," he said, and the relief rang in his voice.

"What now?" said Jim. "Are we starting? If we wait much longer I'll never get there."

"Not yet," said Socker. "It's not light enough yet."

It was not until every stick and stone and piece of timber and every nail and bolt was standing clear and visible that Socker said it was time to move. Sitting there, gazing out, trying to will the daylight back into the sky, Jim had not looked at the other three at all. Now, when he moved, he saw Kevin's face. It certainly had been clawed over in the night and little trickles of blood had run down from the scratches and dried on his cheeks. The thing that had done that to his face was no ghost, and it was no nightmare, either. If they remained here too long it looked as if Kevin would be torn to pieces entirely. It was just as well he could not look at his own face. It was an unnerving sight. Jim saw Socker glance at it, widen his eyes and look again. He began to say something, thought better of it and shut his mouth tight.

9

"BETTER GET A DRINK from the tank before we go," Jim said to Socker. "It'll be hot by the time we get to where the car is."

One by one they cupped their hands at the tank tap. The water might be golden brown, it might be full of microbes, rubbish and dead bodies, but it was water. They drank gratefully, slapping it on their faces and hands.

"Go steady," said Socker. "We could need it again."

"Don't tell me we're coming back?" said Jim.

"Where else are you going till I get the money?" said Socker. It was something Jim had forgotten — that he and Willy were still being held to ransom. It seemed a more fantastic notion than anything that had so far happened to them.

They walked down the veranda steps, Socker leading. They saw now why the day had taken so long to come. A bank of clouds muffled the eastern sky. Overhead it wore a whitish look that could have been cloud, or no cloud at all. The morning round them was still and calm. The air was heavy. As the light intensified, the coolness that had belonged to the dark gave place to a thick, eiderdown kind of warmth that made breathing difficult. One of the qualities of the very white light that was developing was a kind of blackness that seemed to come from behind their own eyes. It was a strange, subaqueous kind of morning that began slowly to draw their nerves tight.

Socker was on the bottom step, about to put his foot on the ground when a squeak from just beneath him made him jump hurriedly off the step and onto the ground. He spun round, and behind him Kevin drew back, blocking the way for Jim and Willy. So, from the edge of the veranda they both saw clearly what happened next. From beneath the bottom step came a kitten. It was a large kitten, but it still retained a great deal of soft, woolly fur and its eyes were very blue. It seemed to have been frightened out of its cover by the footsteps above it for it did not quite know where to go and began padding about in the dust, first this way and then that. It made again the squeak that had alarmed Socker. Now they saw the kitten they recognized the sound as a very kittenish and plaintive mew. But it contained a harsh note unusual in most kittens.

Before anyone had time to say anything at all Socker had pounced on it, caught it by the back legs, swung it

93

round and brought it down with all his strength on the edge of the step. It never made another sound and when he threw it away from him on to the dust of the courtyard it lay quite motionless except for one back leg which twitched twice before straightening out and lying still. The blue eyes were still open and from its mouth a small, glistening ruby drop slid into the dust.

No one moved. No bird uttered and not a leaf among the nearby saplings was stirred by the smallest breeze. The morning halted.

In the silence Socker spoke loudly. "If you do it like that they don't feel a thing."

The words rang through the courtyard. They echoed from every blank wall, back and forth between house and sheds and then beyond. In the total stillness the waves caused by the sound that had come from Socker's throat rolled on, out across the paddocks, in among the timber, over the hills — forever.

Still no one moved. No one made a sound of any kind. And Socker spoke again. "I got a right to kill anything liable to be dangerous."

The sound waves from this second utterance never had a chance because, from the empty sky, from the blank face of the new day there came a clap of thunder. Simultaneously a blue flash dazzled their eyes so that, for a moment, both deaf and blinded, they did not see the piece of corrugated iron slice through the air and land with a burst of light a yard from Socker. When they could see again, the piece of iron was in a thousand identical little squares neatly laid in rows. Socker had not moved but his face was sheet white. The kitten lay untouched in the dust at Socker's feet. Slowly they looked about them. The storm — whatever it was — had gone as quickly as it came. Of the cloud that had brought the clap of thunder and the one flash of lightning there was no sign. The morning went on as before. Except that now the still, cotton-wool air was beginning to move slowly.

Kevin was the first to come to life. "Come on," he shouted. "Let's get out of here." From the second step down he jumped to the ground and raced out of the courtyard, shying away from the mosaic of iron as he went. It was the signal for a panic flight, and they turned and ran, knowing that they must get away from the house and everything it contained. Only Willy, last as usual, halted when he reached the kitten. For a minute he stood looking down at it. Then he squatted, put the palms of both his hands gently on the cooling body and bent his head so that the pale strands of hair hung forward over his forehead, making a brief shroud for the little corpse. Then he lifted his head, looking about him as if expecting to see something move. There was nothing. The other three were already out of sight round the corner and there was no sound or movement in the courtyard. He jumped up and ran after the others.

They waited for him at the gate to the road, and when he arrived pointed without speaking at the iron hinges that still held the gate to the post. The metal in both hinges had melted and run together, forming one solid piece of iron where there had been a socket and a bolt. The gate would never swing again.

They had come down the hill at record speed, without a word. Now, safely in the middle of the road with the house a quarter of a mile away Socker said, "Fairly solid thunderclap, wasn't it? Must have been the stuffy morning."

He spoke in a more amiable voice than he had used

for some time, and Jim knew that he was after reassurance. It was not something Jim could give, even if he had wanted to. Socker sickened him and he did not want to talk to him at all.

But Kevin replied with breathless eagerness. "I never heard anything like it. It fair rocked me. You was lucky, Sock. You could have been struck. Or you could have been chopped by that piece of tin."

This was not the kind of reassurance Socker was after and Kevin's reward was a shove in the back and a request to "Get moving, can't you? We haven't got all day."

Socker started off down the road, his sore feet forgotten. Kevin hurried after him when the gap between them began to widen. Jim turned to look at Willy. He knew Willy had not taken part in the mindless race to the road, and he felt ashamed that at such a time he had deserted him.

As soon as he saw Willy's face he knew that nothing he had done or failed to do had made any difference at all to Willy. At this moment Jim scarcely existed for him. He was in a white-hot rage, but not because of Jim. Beneath the rage there was something more. Jim had never seen him look like this, with the skin drawn tight across his face, showing the sharp line of jaw and cheek bone, the muscles round the mouth rigid, thinning the lips, clenching the teeth. Beneath — behind — the rage a kind of desolation showed through, a sorrow that, surely, could not have been caused by the death of a kitten. Together these emotions were consuming him, but at the same time working in him in a way that made him appear to Jim — taller? Stronger? Powerful was the word that came into his mind.

The hand that he had put out for comfort fell to his

96

side. No comfort could come from him to Willy now. He stepped aside, and though Willy walked past with his eyes wide, falling directly on him, Willy did not see Jim at all, but went on down the road, striding fast, hands thrust deep into his pockets. Jim took a step, opened his mouth to call out, and then shut it again. He stood somehow without power of movement and watched Willy go down the road, watched him catch up to Socker and Kevin, and pass them too, as if he had not seen them. Then he was round the corner and out of sight, and Jim drew in a long breath and started to run down the road.

He caught Socker and Kevin before they turned the corner. He had intended to pass them and go on after Willy, but round the corner there was still no sign of Willy and he had to ease his pace to get his breath back. There was another corner farther on, and once round that he must surely see Willy again. The house was lost to view now, behind the trees. There were only trees in front, behind and on either side. The road, winding, narrow and very rough, became lost among the hills. Willy was not round the next corner, or the next. But still, he could not be far ahead. Only the constant downward slope told Jim they were making always towards the river. The wind that had risen after the thunderclap was blowing constantly now, not strong, but steady, as if it had an aim in view. With the wind had come the clouds, and perhaps the purpose of the wind was to blanket the hills with cloud, for quite soon the distant views were blotted out. Wisps of cloud tangled with the tallest trees, and before long a blowing mist softly tickled their faces and dampened the gum leaves so that they hung more perpendicular from their wiry stems. Having spread the clouds over the land, the wind began to drop, leaving them alone among the settling gloom. The mist got wetter. It became harder to see any distance ahead. Willy could be no more than ten or fifteen yards ahead now and they would not be able to see him. They were enclosed, imprisoned, in the thick, cooling drizzle. The smell of eucalyptus poured from the warm, wet leaves. Around them, among the trees where they could not be seen, the birds were enjoying the change. The sound of them was everywhere and from some deep gully not far away a thrush sang. Walking was easier in the cooler air and Jim, spurred by anxiety, had no trouble keeping up with Socker. Kevin had begun to fall back and was now behind them.

CHAPTER

10

For once Socker had no wish to lead and trudged along beside Jim. Indeed, Jim thought he even welcomed his presence, and once or twice made what for him were friendly remarks. The pecking order had begun to level out again. Jim had no wish to talk and paid little attention to what he was saying. He was trying not to think of Socker. With the last picture of Willy in his mind it was not difficult to forget for quite long periods that Socker was there at all. But there came a time during the morning when Socker's observations became fewer and more disjointed. Strangely, as he became more silent Jim was more aware of his presence.

And it was becoming an uneasy presence. There was always enough vitality about Socker to make his moods apparent, and his mood now was clearly one of heightened awareness, of suspicion and, even, of fear. Jim let himself fall back a little so that he could see Socker more clearly without having to turn his head. His movements had become tight, and his head kept turning slightly as if he were looking from side to side as he walked. Eventually he stopped talking altogether and his stride lengthened. Jim had no trouble falling back now. It was hard to keep up. He did not particularly want to keep up and he allowed the distance between them to increase. This did not suit Socker, and he called over his shoulder, "Can't you walk any faster than that? Look how far ahead your brother's got."

This thought had been the only one occupying Jim's mind since he started, but Socker's comment gave a jolt to fruitless speculations. For the first time Jim wondered, not when he would catch Willy up, but why Willy had gone off and left him. What had so driven Willy that he had been blind, even to his brother?

When Jim's pace remained as it had been, Socker allowed himself to drop back until they were side by side again. They walked on in a tense silence for some time. Jim found it impossible to forget Socker was beside him now. His mood became infectious and finally Jim said, "What's the matter?"

As if he had been waiting to be asked the question Socker said, "I keep wondering if we're being followed."

"Course we are," said Jim. "Kevin's back there."

"I don't mean Kevin," said Socker.

"No one else up here that I know of," said Jim.

"I wasn't thinking of people," said Socker.

Jim said nothing. He recalled Willy's mood. Once

again he forgot Socker was beside him. After a time Socker spoke again, almost, it seemed, against his will.

"It was the same coming back the other night. I thought it'd be all right in the daylight."

"You must be mad," said Jim.

At any other time Socker would not have let such a remark go by. Now it seemed to reassure him.

The mist was thickening, hitting their faces with little globules of moisture more like real raindrops than mist. Even the trees on either side were growing shadowy and still Willy was out of sight ahead. The birds became quieter as visibility lessened. And their own footfalls in the settling gravel were muted too. A furtive sound behind them made them stop and spin round. But it was only Kevin panting to catch up. His eyes were wide and alarmed.

"I thought something was following me," he said.

They walked on in a bunch, close together, and as they walked the hairs at the back of Jim's head began to prickle. Every few minutes he found himself wanting to look round. He did not allow himself to do so, but Kevin's head was moving all the time, from side to side and frequently behind him. Socker walked doggedly on and did not turn his head either, but Jim knew that soon the effort of self control would be too much. Every time Kevin's head moved Jim expected him to say he had seen — something. But he said nothing. Only his breathing became louder and quicker. Even now Jim could not be sure whether the feeling of something behind was real or implanted by the fears of the other two. He could hear nothing but the drip of water from the trees, their own footsteps and an occasional bird. He could see nothing at all, for the mist enveloped them completely now. If anything were following it could be almost on

101

their heels and they would never know unless it made a sound. It came into his mind that he had never heard the cat at home walking about — only the sound of its claws sometimes on the linoleum.

Kevin suddenly shied into him and said, "What's that?"

They all stopped together, back to back, looking outward. "What?" said Socker. "There's nothing."

"I thought I saw that branch move. The one hanging over the road." They all looked up. There was a branch almost over their heads, but it was high up and all they could see was the grey bunches of leaves. Impossible to say if they moved or not. As they looked up a flurry of drops fell on their faces.

"Must have been the wind," said Socker loudly. "Come on."

Jim began to wish he had not allowed Willy to get out of sight. He wondered how soon Willy would come to, and find that Jim was not with him. He felt no confidence it would happen soon. But he knew without a doubt that when he did, Willy would come to the rescue. And it was strange that he felt so much in need of being rescued. Walking with Socker and Kevin was unnerving as well as unpleasant. Willy, he thought, could not be too far away, and he began to walk more quickly with the idea of catching up and leaving the other two behind. But they had no intention of being separated from him and they lengthened their strides with his. They walked on very fast all together. Short of breaking into a run they would be with him until the end.

No one talked any more. Kevin stopped looking round. They kept their eyes on the ground at their feet. With the thickening of the mist Jim had lost all sense of direction. He only knew that they were still going down.

Somewhere, some time, they must come to the river. His burst of speed had made him the leader and the other two walked on his heels. He found himself searching the damp yellow gravel for Willy's footmarks. It was not until he had totally failed to find them that he began to take more notice of his surroundings. He looked up. The trees pressed in closer than ever on either side. The road had deteriorated alarmingly. He realized suddenly it was no longer a road where one could drive a car. Yet Socker had driven the car as far as the river, or so he said. There were no wheelmarks here. There had been no rain since the car had come down. The ground had been hard, but not so hard that here and there a tire track would not show in the dust. In any case — Jim slowly digested the fact — this was no longer the road. He stopped dead and Socker and Kevin closed in on either side.

"What's wrong?" said Socker.

"This isn't the road. We've taken the wrong track in the mist."

They stood in silence and the mist drifted soundlessly about them. On each side the ghosts of trees crowded round, silent too.

"What'll we do?" said Kevin, and it was Jim he asked, not Socker.

"We must go back," said Jim. "Come on. Quick." He thought of Willy, walking down some other road, thinking they were following. But Willy might not yet be thinking of them at all. They needed Willy now. "Come on," he said again. He began to walk back up the hill, but neither Socker nor Kevin seemed eager to follow him. "What are you waiting for?" he said. He found he was reluctant to walk on into the mist alone.

They did not answer, but Kevin said suddenly, "What

did you do with the gun, Socker? Where's the gun?"

For a moment Socker looked as if Kevin had hit him. Then he said slowly, "It's at the house. I forgot it." And it was the first time Jim had heard him admit a mistake.

After that they started, reluctantly, to follow him back along the narrow path. It seemed unbelievable that they could have mistaken the route. The road had at least been clear before them and Socker had been along it more than once before. But the mist had enveloped them, the small rain had perhaps partially blinded them, and fear had lost them their judgement. They had, somewhere, left the road. But it was just a matter of going back. Jim walked on, thinking of Willy. He also thought, with a quickening of the pulse, that if there had been anything following them he might come across it now. He looked about as he walked, alert, keyed up, ready. Nothing moved. The path was empty. Then he stopped and looked down. In the fine, damp gravel at his feet there were the marks of paws. They were facing towards him and there were quite a number of them. They came from as far up the path as he could see and they seemed to be all over the place. At once he thought of the cats, but these were not the marks of any cat. They were far too big. Into his head came Willy's voice. *"They're such big cats."* He walked on, his heart thumping in his chest. He did not want to have to tell the two behind him what Willy had said. He would just go back quickly — until he found Willy.

It seemed a long way to where they had taken the wrong turning. The mist was as thick as ever and their clothes were damp to the skin. There was no end to this narrow, twisting path and he began to wonder how he

104

could ever have gone so far without seeing he was wrong. But the walking was becoming easier. He stepped out with longer strides. Then again he stopped. The path was going downhill. There had been no time since they left the house when they had walked uphill. He felt the first stirrings of panic inside him and pulled himself together. The mist would not last for ever. Some time Willy would miss him. With his knowledge of the country he would at once know where they had gone wrong. But Socker and Kevin had to be told.

"We're wrong again," he said bluntly.

"Eh? Can't be. Come on." Socker went past him, but stopped when he did not follow. "Where could we have gone wrong? There was no other way. Must be right."

"Do you remember walking uphill?" Jim said, and waited for the implication to sink in.

It sank into Kevin first and he said shrilly, "The path's moved. That's what's happened. The path's been moving behind us." He gave a wild little laugh and Socker stepped over to him and slapped him on the cheek. "Cut it out," he said roughly.

It had been a ridiculous thing to say, but in minds already beginning to be uncertain of what was real and what was not, it planted a seed that began to grow. It was a notion that, like a noxious weed, once in the fertile soil of semi-starvation took a big effort to remove. At a time like this, in a place like this, the effort was almost beyond Jim. He only had to look at the faces of the other two to see it was beyond them, too. He did not think they had seen the paw marks and he did not tell them. Instead he said, "Well, what do we do?" Neither answered and he said, "If we go back we're wrong. If we go forward we're wrong. I think we stay here."

105

"No!" screamed Kevin, and the sound, appalling in the silence, was hurriedly smothered by the mist.

Jim sat down in the middle of the path. He would have to wait. He could think of nothing else and he did not care what the other two decided. He did not want to be alone, but he would rather be alone than move on to somewhere — something — he knew was wrong. He had Willy to cling to and he would wait for Willy. Inevitably, after a few struggles of indecision Socker and Kevin sat down with him. They all knew there would be shelter under the trees, but no one suggested leaving the path. They sat together, back to back as they had stood before, and felt more secure so. Jim had long ago lost track of the time. His stomach, that useful alarm clock, was no use now. It had developed a pain that never went, and only increased as time went on. His stomach said, and had been saying for a long time, that it was mealtime. Some time or other, early or late, it would get dark. Would they still be sitting here then? Jim kept telling himself that long before then Willy would have found them.

Time passed. And half an hour — two hours? — later, Kevin said, "What are we waiting *for*?"

"Willy," said Jim, and the answer seemed to satisfy them.

But time continued to pass, and Willy did not come. The paw marks, Jim noticed, were in the damp ground all round them. Incredible that the other two could not have noticed. Jim kept looking into the mist until he felt the eyeballs starting out of his head. He peered up the path and down the path, and into what was visible of the trees on either side. It was odd that when there was something to see, Socker should be the one to see it. He twisted his arm behind him, felt for Jim's elbow, tightened his hand round it and said very quietly, "Look."

Jim looked over his shoulder. Facing Socker a few yards off and on the edge of the path just beside the trees an animal was sitting. It was a cat all right. It must have been a cat, for it was licking its paw and washing its ear just like any other cat. It wiped round behind its ear and even at that moment the inconsequential memory came into Jim's mind of his mother saying, "When Tibs washes behind his ear it's a sign of rain." Willy was right, of course. It was a big cat. It was so big that if Jim had not seen it washing itself he would have thought it was some other kind of animal, perhaps a puma. It was sitting there peacefully enough and although it was clearly watching them, it was doing so in a relaxed and comfortable way like any other contented cat. It was a tortoiseshell and glowed golden against the silvery tree trunks and the silvery mist.

Jim heard a sudden hiss behind him, and almost simultaneously Socker leaned over and clapped the palm of his hand over Kevin's mouth. He used his favourite phrase. "Shut up," he whispered in Kevin's ear.

For a long period, it seemed, they watched the cat and the cat watched them. Sometimes it licked its lips. Sometimes it blinked. Once it got up, stretched, and sat down again. But it watched them all the time. For their part they found it impossible to take their eyes from it. Then Jim got a drop of water in his eye and rubbed it. He rolled both eyes to clear his vision, and his cleared vision showed him another cat. It, also, was in full view and it was lying on the path behind them on the edge of the mist. This one was a grey cat and it melted into the general greyness. It lay with its head on its paws. He might have thought it asleep if

107

its yellow eyes had not been wide open looking at them.

"There's a cat behind us," he whispered to Socker.

Socker had nothing to say, but his face became more tight and strained. Afterwards one of the things Jim was able to remember was the way the raindrops clung like seed pearls to Socker's strong dark hair.

Not long afterwards they picked out two more cats — tabbies — side by side on the other side of the path. Their eyes, too, were fixed on them. Little by little they picked out more and more cats through the shrouding mist. They never saw them come. They never heard them. But, suddenly, there they were. The three huddled figures pressed closer together now, waiting as the cats seemed to be waiting. The only difference was that the cats knew what they were waiting for.

Once Kevin whispered, "They can't be cats. They're too big."

Socker whispered back, "Who cares what you call them. They're there, aren't they?"

Jim wondered what would happen if he simply got up and walked on. Would they let him through? Would they let them all through? He did not think the other two would follow him and when he thought of himself alone in the mist among the cats he knew he could not do it. In any case, going on achieved nothing. He wished Willy would come. He never doubted Willy would come at last.

The mist hung about them, impenetrable, wet and silent. And the cats waited and watched, silent too. There were perhaps ten or twelve visible now and on the damp air came the smell of them; not of tomcat, but the nerve-tingling feral smell of zoo. Every now and then one would get up and shake itself free of raindrops and

108

lie down again, and each time, when they saw the size of the standing cat they huddled a little closer together. On one side of him Jim could feel Socker's body, hard, warm and motionless. On his other side Kevin pressed even closer, and he was cold and beginning to tremble. The mist began to get thicker. It hung dark and oppressive overhead and pushed in on all sides. It was harder to see the cats now, but the cats apparently had no trouble seeing them, for they moved no closer. A kind of bubble burst inside Jim when he realized the mist was getting no thicker. It was simply that the light was fading. It was getting dark. The night was coming and soon they would be able to see nothing at all. Then they would be helpless. But the cats — the cats could see in the dark. The lack of light made no difference to them.

It was when it had become too dark to see the cats' eyes glowing that Kevin lost his nerve. They had been sitting silent and still for so long, the target of so many yellow eyes, conscious that each tiny movement any of them made was seen and noted. Kevin had begun to whimper softly, saying his bitten hand was throbbing and that he felt ill. As usual Socker said, "Shut up." This time it had the opposite effect. Kevin jumped up, began to make high, incomprehensible sounds and started to run down the road. In a moment he had disappeared into the mist, but they could hear his feet, still running. At the same time, as if this was what they had been waiting for, the cats came to life. They were all on their feet before Kevin had been swallowed by the mist, and Jim saw several of them bound down the road after him.

Jim shouted, "Kevin, stop!" but his voice hardly carried at all through the mist. There were still cats surrounding them, and these began to move now, closing in and making a high, wavering singing sound, eerie and sinister in the deepening night. There was no chance of following Kevin if they had wanted to. At any moment they would be doing battle on their own account. Then, just as Kevin's voice reached a higher, shriller note, something rushed out of the mist on their other side. For a moment, pressed as he was, his senses strained to their limit, Jim thought the figure that sprang towards them was taller than any normal person had a right to be, and that there was a flickering light about it. Then he blinked and looked again, and it was only Willy, running towards them and shouting in a commanding voice. As he reached them the cats drew back and their singing stopped.

"Come with me," said Willy. "We'd better get to Kevin." He ran on, and Jim and Socker followed.

They ran onto Kevin almost before they saw him. He was still screaming and there were cats all round him. One had his injured hand in its mouth and another had him by the ankle. So far they had done no more. Now, as Willy arrived, they let go and drew back. But they stood, watching, tails twitching, while Kevin sank to the ground and moaned.

"I knew you'd come," said Jim.

"Get up," Willy said to Kevin. "You're not hurt." Kevin stopped moaning and got up, nursing his hand. "It wasn't you they're after. But you shouldn't have run. Don't you know a cat will always chase anything that runs?"

"What are they after, then?" said Socker.

Willy turned and faced him. He still looked tall in the deceptive half-light. "I think they're after you, Socker," he said.

Jim was looking closely at Willy. The anger was gone.

110

The grimness remained, and beneath it, still, the sense of a powerful emotion beaten down, controlled, but now guiding every action. The blind look in the eyes had gone, but somehow they had hardened. Willy was nobody's prisoner any more. Jim said almost with diffidence, "Come on. Let's go back, Willy."

Then, at last, Willy turned to look at him. A kind of smile forced its way through the grimness. "Yes," he said. "We'd better. Come on." He turned and began to walk back and the mist parted as he went.

This time Jim made sure to keep beside him. "Is it far?" he asked.

"Far enough," said Willy. "What happened?"

"We don't know," said Jim. "We don't know where we are now. We just, somehow, got here and forward wasn't right and backward wasn't right, so we just stayed and waited for you. At least I did, and Socker and Kevin waited with me."

"There are lots of little tracks," said Willy vaguely.

"You should never have left us," said Socker.

"Look," said Willy. He stopped and turned round so that he was face to face with Socker. "I do what I like. You've got no rights here, Socker. If you haven't learnt it already you'll pretty soon find out. I came back for my brother. It was your good luck you were with him."

"I got a right to know —" began Socker, goaded.

But Willy interrupted him. "You ask those cats what rights you've got, Socker. If you don't know now, they'll show you. They'll show you anyway before we're out of this, I shouldn't wonder — in spite of me." Here was the anger again, blazing out. It stopped Socker in his tracks. Then Willy nodded to Jim and continued on. Jim fell in beside him. Socker and Kevin followed without a word. The cats melted into the darkness.

111

They began to outdistance Socker and Kevin, and when they were out of earshot Jim said softly, "Willy —"

Willy looked at him, saw the expression on his face and said, "You mustn't worry so. It's not your business."

"What do you mean, not my business? What business? Willy, what's happening? Surely a kitten . . ." Immediately he saw the change come over Willy's face. Then it *was* the kitten. Without thinking he said, "What's one wild kitten, anyway?"

"It's a life," said Willy. "Same as yours and mine — and Socker's. It wasn't doing any harm." Suddenly as they walked he clutched Jim's arm and pulled him closer. "Jim, it wasn't only the kitten. These cats have never seen people — only me. I never hurt them and they never hurt me. Now Socker's shown them people are dangerous. What's going to happen now? Jim — " And he said again, "There are so many cats."

"Then they can look after themselves, can't they?" Jim wanted above all to move that expression from Willy's face.

"And what happens to animals that think they can defend themselves against people?"

Jim knew the answer to that, and thought better of giving it. But he said, "It was only once, and maybe Socker . . ."

"Socker," said Willy, "will make a point of coming back with a shotgun the minute he gets the chance." He stopped abruptly and then added, "If he gets back."

"Willy!"

Jim almost stopped, but Willy pulled him on so that the distance between the two walking couples remained the same. He began to talk in a strained, agitated way, as if the words could not be stopped. "I wanted to go. I wanted to go on. I knew if I left them — if I were out of

112

the way — the cats would — do something. I didn't know what, did I? It wasn't my business to know. I could go, and everything would settle itself and it would all be just as it was. But, see, Jim, you stayed with them. When I knew, I had to come back."

It was a long time before Jim was able to understand exactly what Willy was saying. Even Willy, he thought, had not faced the thought directly, had not taken it to its clear conclusion. They had gone quite a long way through the mist before Jim said, "You mean — the cats would have killed them?"

Just saying it aloud seemed to send a tremor through the air about them. Having said it, Jim could say nothing more and he had given up hope of Willy's answer by the time it came.

"How do I know what a wild cat would do?"

Jim was certain that he knew very well and, suddenly, he felt cold. At last he said, "Then it was lucky I stayed."

After that they walked in silence. Socker and Kevin had closed in behind them. It was almost as if they had heard the conversation. Willy, with Jim beside him, led the way, striding along the path as if it were his own front drive. Kevin nursed his injured hand and sighed tremulously from time to time. He seemed to be trying to step exactly in Willy's footsteps. They reached the main road sooner than Jim had expected. He never learnt how it was they had gone wrong when it seemed impossible to do so. Afterwards he put it down to hunger. They turned left and began once again to walk downhill. They could have walked four abreast, but the formation remained as it had been and Socker and Kevin stayed behind.

The mist began to clear and little by little as it cleared

the moon shone through, milky at first and alternately strong and weak as the mist curtains rolled overhead. Then, as unexpectedly as it had come, the mist vanished. The road, the trees and far away in front of them the distant hills were bathed in the light of the full moon. With the dissolving of the mist the total silence that had enveloped them since its coming was gone too. The small sounds of the bush night filled the air again. The world came alive once more. And nothing moved among the trees beside them. Only once, when the path from which they had emerged was a long way behind, came the harsh, singsong miaow of a big tomcat. It could have been a long way away, but it carried, desolate and haunting, on the moonlit air. Behind him Socker's footsteps broke rhythm and faltered, but quickly recovered. Kevin said, "Willy," and trod on his heels.

Willy gave no sign that he had heard anything, but walked on, and Jim walked with him.

Socker said, "How much farther, Willy?" And Jim thought he should have known. But he was asking Willy and his voice was respectful.

"A mile or so," said Willy. "You'll hear the river first. It echoes in that gorge so you can hear it for miles."

Now that they could see the road and the road was downhill, walking was easy. Jim found that it had become so easy that he scarcely bothered to touch the ground any more. He was floating along pleasantly over the surface, only touching down now and then to gain impetus. It was like swimming in moonlight instead of water and it was a pleasing sensation. He saw Willy turn his head once to look at him and then felt a hand under his elbow. How kind of Willy, he thought. And how pleasant to let Willy do the worrying for a change. Then

114

a humming started in his head and gradually grew louder. And after a long, long time he realized the humming had turned to a distant roar, and it was not in his head at all, but was the river roaring up at them from its bend at the bottom of the cliffs where the road ended.

There, ahead of them, sitting in the middle of a wide clearing that was terminated by the cliff edge was the car. In the moonlight it looked like a large blackcurrant cough lozenge. It looked part of the landscape and as if it would never move again. As soon as he saw it Socker ran forward into the clearing, fell on the trunk and opened it.

From far away Jim heard Willy's voice. "I thought it might have been locked." And he felt himself enveloped in a soft, warm black nothing.

Struggling out of the nothing was not quite as pleasant as sinking into it. His head ached, he felt rather sick and he seemed to be stiff all over. But Willy was beside him and was saying, "Come on. Drink it for heaven's sake." He opened his mouth and it was filled with cold chicken soup. He swallowed, and suddenly was awake, sitting up and grabbing at the tin Willy was holding to his mouth.

It was only half a tinful, but when Willy offered him some more he knew he had had enough. "But I'm hungry," he heard himself saying. "I must want more."

He found it had been the same with all of them. They had descended on the food like crows, ravenous, but after a few mouthfuls had found they could eat no more. "Never mind," said Willy. "There's plenty there. We'll eat it when we want to." He turned to Socker. "I thought you said there wasn't much. You must have reckoned on hanging on to us a terribly long time."

115

"Something musta told me," said Socker, and, unexpectedly, he smiled.

It was still night but the moon was low on the western horizon and hung, orange-yellow among the branches of the trees. There was more shadow than moonlight in the clearing now, and in the east the first opalescent glow behind the darkness promised that the sun was soon going to rise. It had been a long night. Willy, Jim and Socker were lying on the dry grass beside the open door. Kevin, taking no chances, was on the back seat and already asleep. There were a hundred questions to be asked and answered, but no one asked them, and Willy, whom Jim expected to give the answers, was lying on his back with his eyes closed, peaceful, relaxed, and as if he had no wish but to be where he was, doing what he was doing. Socker lay on his other side and he, too, was at peace. He lay on his side facing Willy with his knees drawn up, one arm curled against his chest and the other stretched along the ground, as if, in sleep, he were reaching for Willy. To look closely at the face of a sleeping person is always to take a liberty, to encroach on privacy, but Jim, who had never wanted to study Socker before, now found himself curious and raised himself on his elbow to look at the tranquil face. In the half light it looked darker than ever. The hunger of the past days had hollowed out the normally well-fleshed cheeks and unaccustomed peace had smoothed the habitual frown so that the eyes looked farther apart, the eyebrows over them forming a gentler curve. But even at peace and asleep it was not a weak face. Drained, as it was now, of its arrogance, suspicion and the hint of cruelty, it was even an impressive face. It showed, Jim thought, what Socker might have been.

The moon pulled in its last anemic beams, left the

116

clearing and sank beneath the distant trees, and the east grew bright, charging the sky with floods of changing colour — cyclamen, lilac, lemon, tomato and blazing red. And the sun flashed over the eastern rim. The clearing, for such a short space in total darkness, now sent its shadows streaking in the opposite direction and sunlight touched the seeded tops of the dry grass and penetrated the outer walls of the scrub on the western side of the clearing. The night air, which had carried pungent scents of living vegetation and dewy earth now lost its tang, mellowed and grew warm. And all four boys forgot their hunger, forgot the events of the night, forgot both past and future and fell into a long, deep sleep.

11

I<small>T WAS HEAT</small> that woke Jim at last. He was lying on his back with the sun full on his face. He blinked, squinted in the glare and rolled over. Beside him Willy was sitting, knees drawn up and clasped by his arms with his chin resting on top of them. As his habit was, he gazed thoughtfully at the prospect in front of him. His face still bore the calm confidence it had shown last night. Beside him Socker lay on his side, but now his eyes were open and they were fixed on Willy. It was not a hostile look, but somewhere in that steady relaxed regard there was a question. There was no sound or movement from the car. The morning was calm and still. The sun was already clear of the trees and hung, pouring light and heat onto the clearing from a good third of the way along its trajectory. The grass stems round them stood rigid and motionless, silently popping their tiny seeds out of the drying, retracting husks onto the baked earth beneath. No leaf moved on the surrounding trees. Only the river, out of sight at the bottom of the cliffs, continued to fill the air with its muted thunder. It took Jim a minute or two to hear it, for he had grown accustomed to its constant sound.

Socker saw him move and sat up quickly. "He's awake now, Willy," he said briskly. "What about some tucker?"

Willy lifted his head, glanced at Jim to confirm it for himself and got up. Standing, feet apart, head thrown back, he stretched, yawned and sighed. From Jim's worm's eye view he looked enormous. "OK," he said. "If you don't mind waking your friend Kevin."

Socker laughed and stood up beside him. "Kevin knows how to look after himself. None better. He'll sleep if he wants to, but not if there's something being handed out. He'll be there when the trunk's opened." As Jim got up he said, "See, we couldn't move till you woke. Boss's orders. I thought we'd starve to death there for a while." The hectoring tone had gone from his voice. It occurred to Jim that this was the first time he had ever seen Socker looking happy, and wondered how, with his plans in ruins, this could be so.

They moved over to the car and Socker opened the trunk. Even now, it was still Socker's car. Jim looked in at the window. Kevin was lying on his back. His right arm and leg hung down to the floor, his left leg, bent to accommodate his body on the seat, was leaning against the back and the bandaged hand was across his chest.

119

His mouth was open, his eyes closed, and the pale lashes lay blindly, featherlike, across the lower lid. His face was no longer waxen, but bright pink. He muttered and twitched as he slept. Suddenly, perhaps disturbed by the opening of the trunk, his eyes flew open, became aware of Jim's face at the window and grew wider still. Kevin shot upright, bumped the bandaged hand on his bent knee and gave a yelp. Jim opened the door.

"I'm not going to eat you, but there's food if you want it." He had no liking for Kevin, but there was something about him now that roused a reluctant pity.

It took Kevin a long time to scramble out, and he did so muttering and grumbling. He took no notice of Jim but tottered straight up to Willy. "I'm thirsty," he said.

It was hot beside the car, in the middle of the clearing, and they took what they wanted and went over to the shade of the trees. In the totally revealing light of day there seemed nothing at all that the trees could be concealing. At this hour of the morning there was no mystery, no danger anywhere. The night with its confusion, fear and bafflement was gone — dissolved like the mist — and this was another ordinary day. They sat and ate, and drank soft drinks. And Jim could feel his sense of order restored, his vitality rise in direct relation to the increasing comfortable feeling in his stomach.

Socker apparently had the same feelings, for when he had finished eating he said, "Now I've got to make some plans." He sounded almost reluctant to do so, and paused as if he hoped someone would persuade him not to. But when he continued it seemed that he had already made them. "I've got to find that crossing again." He stopped and looked at Willy, but Willy made no sign and he went on, "I reckon I know where it is. Can't say how long I'll be. Depends how soon I cross. Kevin —" He waited until Kevin, who was sitting on the other side of Willy, reluctantly looked in his direction. "You got to go with Jim and Willy back to the house. You'll all carry as much of the food as you can." This time, when he waited for a reply, Kevin spoke.

"I'm not going and you can't make me. I'm staying by this car. I'm sick."

Before Socker could say any more Willy said, "I'm not going either, Socker, and neither is Jim. Now you haven't got the rifle you can't make any of us."

Jim watched Socker's face change colour, the veins on his forehead swell, then, curiously, what must have been the biggest effort at self-control Socker had ever made. Gradually his face resumed its normal colour and he said , "And what's your plan?"

"Plan?" said Willy. "You're the one with plans, Socker. I'm just going to stay here, where the food is, and the river water. Jim'll stay too."

Jim spoke now. "Anyway, Kevin *is* sick, Socker. I think it's his hand. Let's have a look, Kevin." He went and knelt beside Kevin, who shrank closer to Willy, nursing his hand.

"Don't be a nit," said Willy. "Show it to him. Jim's the best doctor here."

Reluctantly Kevin allowed Jim to take his wrist, balance it on his knee and undo the bandage. "It hurts," he said. "Throbs, like."

The bandage came off more easily than Jim had expected, but the wound beneath, moist, swollen and encircled with red flesh, did not look good. It was not going to heal, and somewhere deep inside it the cat's fang had carried a fair-sized dollop of infection. Jim tore yet another strip off the tail of Kevin's shirt and wrapped it up gently. "Someone'll have to go down to the river sometime," he said. "We got to clean out this bite or Kevin'll probably blow up and bust. It's gone bad."

Kevin gave a small moan and pressed the hand again to his chest. Socker stood up. "So you stay here," he said. "One of you can go for some water sometime. I'm going to find the crossing."

Jim looked up at him and said, "Socker —"

"Well?"

"If you get across, what are you going to do then?"

"What I told you. Ring your dad."

"Then what? Suppose he gives you the money, then what? How do you get us out of here?"

Socker's eyes narrowed. "Same way I got out, I suppose — if I get out."

Jim was about to say, "What's to stop us getting out that way too, after you've gone," when he knew suddenly that Willy was looking at him. He shut his mouth, and Willy looked away.

"I'll be back," said Socker, and turned and started to walk across the clearing.

Willy got up and took several steps after him, so that he was standing in the open, clear of the trees, under the sky. "Socker," he said. He did not speak loudly, but Socker stopped at once. "We've all got to get out, somehow, soon. Your plan won't work now, Socker, but we've still got to get out. You want to go alone?" For reply Socker started to walk again, faster this time. "You watch out then, that's all." The last words were shouted, and at the same time from somewhere deep among the trees a flock of screaming galahs took to the air and began to swoop in great circles — pink bellies bright in the sunlight — round the clearing and above the cliffs. As if triggered by the galahs, a flock of twenty or thirty sulphur-crested cockatoos rose on snow-white wings from the trees on the far side and, with ear-splitting cries, joined the flight of galahs. For a few minutes the sky was filled with hurtling, screaming birds, blocking the sun, battering the eardrums and describing swift, feathered circles overhead. As Jim jumped up it seemed that the centre of their narrowing circles was Willy, who stood with his head up, watching them fly. Pink bellies, white bellies, wings beating the air, indescribable noise, a sense of the whole sky in motion. And Jim had a sudden sensation that he, too, had left the ground. Then his head began to spin, he became giddy and fell. On the other side of the clearing Socker, his hands to his ears, ran for cover. The birds wheeled, shrieking, and then, as quickly as they had come, flew off to the trees. Only Willy was left standing alone in the open clearing.

Jim sat up and found Willy standing over him. "I warned him, didn't I? You can't say I didn't warn him."

There was something that needed saying, and slowly, trying to control the buzzing in his ears, Jim managed to say it. "I don't think anything of Socker, but I can't see how his life going the same way as the kitten's makes it any better. If it's the cats you care about, think what'd happen if — if. . . . Then they *would* come with guns, the police and all." He wanted to tell Willy to come back to earth, to say that they couldn't just let Socker go off to die, if that was what was going to happen. But even as he thought of it, it seemed too impossible, too like a bad dream, to be true. Willy must be out of his mind — perhaps the shock of seeing the kitten. Jim had always thought he'd been born with a skin too few. But Willy was turning away, walking slowly back to the shade of the trees. Jim got up and followed him.

123

AFTER THE BRIEF commotion the silence hummed in the cars. Socker had gone. Kevin was lying propped against a tree, and as Willy walked towards him he raised his head. Jim was near enough to hear him say, "What's going to happen about me hand? I'm not going to die, am I?" And to hear Willy's reply, "I don't think *you're* going to die."

"No one's going to die," Jim said with tremendous confidence. "All this talk of dying. Anyone'd think it was a South American jungle. This is Australia, remember? Where there's nothing to hurt in the bush, only snakes. And who's afraid of a few cats, anyway?" Now that his stomach was full and the sun was shining, the happenings of the night before were becoming more and more like ordinary midnight horrors, something that vanishes with the light. They had not even tried saying, "Shoo!" to the cats.

"But me hand," said Kevin. "It's poisoned."

"Oh, your hand," said Willy. He thought for a moment and then said, "I know where there's some water. There's a bit of a creek. I'll be back." He went to the car, took a mug from the trunk and went off into the scrub.

He was only away some twenty minutes, but by the time he returned Kevin had dropped off to sleep and Jim had begun to wonder whether something more than water had taken Willy off again. He was relieved when Willy reappeared carrying the mug. He put it down carefully and they moved off to where they could talk without being overheard if Kevin should wake. Even before they had sat down Jim said, "Will Socker get across?"

"No."

"So what, Willy?"

"So I suppose he'll have to come back. What else can he do?"

"He might have a look for somewhere else. He might just go on till he finds a place, however long it takes him."

"He might, but I think he'll come back first. He'll need food, won't he?"

"I suppose so. Willy, do you know a place to cross?"

After a long silence Willy said, "There is a way, where the cats cross. Socker wouldn't know about it, and you wouldn't want to do it unless you had to. There's a fallen tree over one of the narrow parts. There's a drop

125

on the other side and the tree didn't look too strong. I've never been across because I couldn't get back. But now —"

"We wouldn't want to get back, would we?" Jim had been leaning back against a log, but now he sat up straight.

"That was the way I thought we'd go," said Willy simply.

"We could go now." Jim was up on his knees.

"You forget Kevin," said Willy without moving. "He's a creep but he is sick. And he is by his silly self till Socker gets back."

"But we've got a chance now, and when Socker comes back it'll be gone."

"It'll be harder, but it won't be gone. Not while he doesn't know there's another way." Willy stopped and looked at Jim. "You say, Jim. We'll do what you say."

With the decision thrust back at him Jim said without thinking, "We've got a right —" He stopped, at once reminded of Socker. He sank back against the log, frowning, and with great concentration began to dig a hollow in the ground with the heel of his shoe. At last he said, "We'll wait then, Willy."

They waited while the sun climbed to the zenith and began its downward journey. Kevin woke, complained, and had his hand dressed. Jim could not think it did much good, but it gave Kevin confidence. They offered him food, but he was not hungry, and soon he went to sleep again.

They found themselves something to eat and ate it in the shade far enough from Kevin not to be overheard, near enough to watch him. But with the immediate future so doubtful, there was little to say. The small things that had made up their lives until now had

126

become too small to talk about, their present situation too painful and too vast.

Willy spoke once. "I been thinking." The pause was so long that Jim thought that was all he intended to say. But then he spoke again, very slowly. "What you said about the killing. Once it starts it might never stop. It would only grow. I see now . . . " He was looking across the clearing into the blazing, still afternoon, but he was not seeing the clearing at all. He was seeing something else, less pleasant, less peaceful. "I see now what you meant. It mustn't go any farther. We mustn't let Socker —"

Jim said quickly, "Socker's all right now, isn't he? You said . . . "

Willy wrenched his gaze from whatever it had been fixed on and turned to Jim. "He's safe enough in the daytime — unless anything kind of happens — like the mist you got caught in. He'll be all right. So long as he comes back."

The sick feeling that Jim had thought himself cured of came again. If Willy still thought, now in the frank, unshadowed, open afternoon, that there was danger he must have some reason for thinking so. "Willy, are you *sure?*"

"I'm not sure," said Willy quickly. "I'm not sure, but I'm afraid."

It was the longest afternoon Jim ever remembered. On the far side of the clearing near the cliff's edge and parallel with it the road went on down to the river. Only the first ten yards or so were visible because of the downward slope. Starting out down the slope, diminishing until only his head had been in their line of sight, Socker had gone when the day was still fresh. Jim kept looking at the spot now, waiting for the reappearance of that dark head and believing at least a dozen times that he

127

saw it. But Socker did not come back.

"Could he have got across after all?" Jim said once.

"Not where he thinks he can," said Willy. "See, the river's risen a lot since he was there last. Socker would never think of a thing like that."

As the afternoon went on the sound of the river became louder. It filled the emptiness and became the one dominant sound where, earlier, it had been only the bass accompaniment to the sound of birds and insects and to the rustling of leaves above their heads. Jim realized now that all these noises had stopped. The river's was the only sound to be heard. Then, quite quickly, the sunlight vanished. He thought at first that the afternoon was over. But he looked to the west and saw that a long bank of clouds was pushing up from the undulating horizon. One bright spot showed where the sun had just been blotted out. Long beams radiated from the brightness, streaming from below a blue-black ceiling. With bright, white fingers they touched the sombre hills below, like spotlights in the rapidly increasing gloom.

"We're in for a storm, I think," said Jim.

Willy had been lying beside him all afternoon, but now there was no answer and Willy was gone. He was some distance off, walking about the clearing, looking at the sky, looking at the trees, scanning the ground. After a time he returned. "Socker's not back," he said.

"We're in for a storm," said Jim.

"I think so too." And Willy repeated, "Socker's not back."

"It's still light," said Jim.

"Remember I said he'd be all right in daylight so long as nothing happened?"

"Nothing has happened."

"If the storm came. . . ."

128

"Would that be 'something', what you meant?"

"See, things get sort of excited in a storm. Worked up."

"You mean — you really mean the cats might go for him if the storm came?" Jim only had to look at Willy's face to find the answer. "Then what'll we do?"

"I think we'd better go after him — quick."

Jim got up. "Pity to wake that Kevin, but I suppose we can't leave him there."

"We can't leave him there," said Willy, and walked quickly towards him.

Kevin had just woken and was complaining that his hand hurt like hell and that he was thirsty.

"Can't be too bad if you slept all afternoon," said Jim.

He did not want to be moved. It was going to be agony to get up. He doubted if he would be able to. But after they had found him something to drink and threatened to drag him to the car if they couldn't carry him, he got, tottering, to his feet.

"We've got to go and look for Socker," said Jim. "We could leave you if you want, but it's going to storm and we mightn't be back till after dark." It was surprising how these simple statements sent the vitality pouring back into Kevin's limbs. He walked quite briskly to the car. But he complained as he went. They had no call to look for Socker. Come to think of it, it was pretty funny they should bother. Socker would come in his own good time. Socker told them to stay with him and they could see he needed them. They must be mad, going off at this time of day. He muttered his way to the car, and was still muttering as they got him onto the back seat and shut the door.

"Lock it from inside," said Willy, peering in at the window. "Go on. Lock it." They waited while he scrambled round, locking each door in turn. They did not wait to see him settled on the seat.

"Come on," said Willy. "Quick."

They crossed the clearing and took up the road where it left the open ground – the way Socker had gone. Between the road and the edge of the cliff there was only a narrow strip of low-growing scrub and they were able to see halfway down the steep rocky slopes on the far side. The river itself was not visible from the road, but they could hear it clearly enough, for the sound of rushing water echoed from cliff to cliff. After a time the slope became steeper, the cliffs became less sheer and the distance from one bank to the other widened. It was possible to see a long way ahead over the hills to the open land to the east. And in the east the sky was still clear and blue. Behind them the first faint rumble of thunder came like a whispered threat.

They had gone perhaps a quarter of a mile when the land on their left began to rise again. The road continued down towards the river, but the sloping ground that carried it began to narrow.

Willy stopped. "I think we should separate here," he said.

"Separate?" said Jim. "What for?" He thought he had come to keep Willy company, and he did not care much for the idea of walking through wild and unknown country by himself.

"All you have to do is follow the road," said Willy. "There's a kind of cliff again a bit farther on and I thought if I kept to the top and you kept to the bottom we'd see more between us."

"But Socker would have kept to the road."

"So he would, I expect, but — anyway, the road stops when it gets to the river. Socker was going on down. He'd know he couldn't cross where the road did and he'd have found out he couldn't get over where he meant to."

"Willy, why do you say, 'was'?"

Willy's eyes widened. "I don't know. I didn't know I had."

"OK," said Jim suddenly. "You go up and I'll go down. What happens when I get to the river? Do I go on down too?"

"I expect so," said Willy. And again, "I expect so. We'll know when we get that far. But — I think we will." He did not say anything more but left Jim and pushed his way through the roadside undergrowth and began to climb the slope. There were trees here, too, but the soil was poor and they were smaller and farther apart. It was quite possible to see through them.

Jim walked on down the rutted road. The tracks Socker's motor bike had made in April or May had long since vanished. There were no signs of any other vehicle. But, now he looked carefully, there were signs here and there of Socker's footprints. He might have known Willy would be right. But if he were right in this, he might — must — be right about everything else. And the cats — and the storm. Jim started to walk faster. There was still no sign of Socker, but there was another loud rumble of thunder and he stopped and looked behind him. The cloud bank was impenetrable and covered the whole of the western quarter. Mostly it was a deep, bruised, blue-black, but here and there lighter, frolicsome clouds like tufts of cotton-wool drifted across in front of the dark wall. In places they ruffled the surface of their background so that, to Jim's apprehensive imagination, the cloud bank took on the appearance of a huge scaled monster rising from behind the western horizon, spreading and brooding over all the empty land about him. As he watched a flash of white light burst from the monster's belly and afterwards it growled at him. He

131

took a breath, pulled himself together, turned, and went on. And the storm climbed up the sky behind him.

From time to time he looked to his left, and he could still see Willy making his way over the rising undulations, always remaining within sight of Jim and the river. And now it was possible to see glimpses of the river itself. A brown, swirling flood, frothing here and there with foam, it surged down between high rocks, still some distance below the road. The idea that any vehicle should cross that savage torrent seemed absurd. He hurried on, always downward and nearer to the river. The afternoon was very dark now. The thunder came more frequently and more loudly, and even with his back to the storm Jim could tell when the lightning flashes came. There had been no wind, but now little puffs brought the smell of wet earth with it.

By the time Jim reached the point where the road disappeared into the river the storm was overhead. The small puffs had turned to gusts and the gusts had turned to a gale that bent the trees and flung dead leaves and strips of bark high in the air. The thunder no longer rumbled, but exploded overhead like bombs, and the lightning was constant, dazzling and simultaneous with the thunder. The rain that up to now had done no more than bring the dust up in front of him in little silent spurts came pouring down, flattening the ground and pressing all the small plants back into the wet earth. Jim, standing on the brink of the river, was already so wet that taking cover was a pointless exercise. No one could help but be afraid of the violence overhead, but there was no cover, no place to run and no protection. So he stood where he was, blinking and holding his ears. He could see Willy standing against the skyline looking towards him, and Willy was not taking cover either.

There came a clap of thunder louder than ever and with it a flash of lightning that, as Jim looked, seemed to envelop Willy so that he stood suddenly against the tormented sky, enormous and incandescent. At the same moment he raised his arms, and Jim dazzled, deafened, overwhelmed by what was going on round him, had a sudden terrifying vision of Willy, part of the whole elemental upheaval, being borne up into the sky, to disappear forever.

It was a momentary illusion and then, when the lightning went leaving Willy still standing there, his normal size, and apparently shouting (though no sound was audible), Jim saw that he had raised his arms and was waving them and pointing urgently downstream. Obedient, unquestioning, Jim left the road and pushed on down the river bank, fighting his way through twisted grasses, spiky shrubs and wiry lengths of creeper. Everything that grew was wet and everything that grew seemed to wrap itself about him, grasping his clothes, tearing at his legs, slapping him in the face. He fought on and began to make some headway. The ground became more rocky and the plants fewer, and he saw that the river now flowed among tumbled rocks, those in the middle of the river heaving up through the current, their sides washed smooth, catching the light like patent leather. On both banks the piles of rock presented almost insurmountable obstacles. In the fast disappearing daylight it was hard to see if there was a way through, or round them, but he kept on, hoping that the reason for his efforts would become clear in time.

It was when the worst of the storm was passing over and he was at last clear of the vegetation that he saw what Willy must have seen ten minutes earlier. On top of one of the piles of rock ahead of him Socker was

133

standing. All round him, clambering, clawing, leaping, there were cats. Once again Jim was appalled at their size. These were wild animals, angry and dangerous, and they were after Socker. If ever their forebears had been domesticated cats they had forgotten it now. They had their quarry cornered and they were going to pull him down. They were making chilling sounds of triumph as they swarmed up the rocks. The noise resembled the familiar sounds of a cat fight increased, magnified, many times. And with the yowling and screeching there was a deeper note which ordinary cats do not make, but which wild animals intent on their prey do. Jim could feel himself freezing, his eyes fixed, and knew this was the note that halted game in its tracks, making it easy to tear down. He forced himself on — towards all those exposed teeth and claws, towards Socker, who made no sound at all, but fought them off as they came, wielding a stick he must have picked up as he ran for the rock. Jim wondered how far he had run with the cats behind him, how soon he had known they were following him, and why.

He wondered how long Socker had stood there already — how much longer he would be able to stand. Some of the cats were now within reach of his boots. He began to kick. He had both hands on the stick, and even as Jim watched, a cat caught the end of it between the teeth and began to worry it. Socker wrenched it away and struck the cat over the head. But there were others, dodging the flying boots, reaching with claws extended for the foot he stood on. His face was putty-white and glistening, and strands of black hair clung to his forehead. But Jim could see that his teeth were clenched, and still he made no sound.

Jim started to run, looking for a weapon as he went.

He was half way across the open ground when he picked up a short, sturdy piece of wood. Then he shouted to Socker and ran faster than he had ever run on the football field. Socker must have heard the shout above the shrieking of the cats, for he flung up his head, saw Jim, and with that moment's inattention allowed one of them to spring onto his back. He staggered, bent forward to shake off the cat, and another leapt on to his hip, clinging with claws and teeth. After that Jim saw only a rising surge of cats, a seething mound of furry bodies. And then the whole mass toppled, leaned outwards and disappeared down the far side of the rock. In front of the rock the cats divided into two streams, making for the melee behind, encircling the rock like a tide. The sounds that they made lessened. The screeching grew less, the singsong note vanished altogether. But in their place came a snarling sound infinitely more blood-curdling. Jim hurled himself forward. It would be a question of minutes now. Not once did it occur to him that he could be the second victim, though he did have one fleeting wish that Willy were nearer.

He reached the rock gasping for breath, bounded over the boulders at its foot, round the other side — and saw him.

Socker was not done yet. He was down, half on a small rock and still fighting. His face was streaked with blood and he was struggling to protect his throat. Jim flung himself in among the cats. He hardly felt it when a pair of teeth closed round his arm. It was his left arm, and he continued to wield the stick with his right. Unaware that he was dragging one of the cats with him, he pushed his way forward. Once or twice as the cats totally blocked his path he doubted if he would get there in time. But he fought on, scarcely noticing the pain in

135

his arm, or the cat that still swung from it, Then, suddenly, there came a gap as two of the cats fell backwards, and Jim, struggling through it, found himself beside Socker.

Socker now lay on his stomach over the rock, his arms round his head. One leg was somehow underneath him. The other still kicked out blindly. There were two cats on top of him but for the moment the others had drawn back, waiting for some kind of signal to attack again. The cat that had attached itself to Jim's arm dropped off and retreated to where the others waited. Jim began to shout. Afterwards he could not remember what it was he shouted, but as he did so he jumped forward brandishing his stick at the two cats on Socker's body. For a moment they crouched with their eyes fixed on him and their claws in Socker's back. In just such a position Jim had often seen their own cat crouch over a bird when Willy had tried to take it from her. Still shouting he hit them, first one and then the other, across the nose, saw them blink, snarling, and then saw first one and then the other release its hold. As he took up a position across Socker's body they drew back. But when he struck them again each paused to crouch and snarl and he could not be sure that they would not spring again. He beat them down off the rock in the end and stood straddling Socker alone on top of it. But there were cats all round and the two at his feet were still within springing distance and he knew that he could not hold his position forever. In desperation he raised his head and shouted, "Willy!"

He heard the answer from quite near at hand. "Coming. Don't move."

Willy came running, but just before he reached the cats he slowed to a walk. They, too, had heard his voice

136

and for an instant they froze. Every cat's head turned to watch him come. They made no further movement, but Jim thought that some of the wild fury began to drain from them. Little by little their coats ceased to stand on end, their tails grew still. Only the two at Jim's feet kept their eyes on him and not Willy, and their tails continued to twitch. Willy walked steadily forward and as he drew near he talked to the cats. Jim could not hear the words and in the end concluded that there were no words. It was the tone they seemed to understand, and as he reached them they drew back a little, lifting their heads as he brushed past. Once he dropped his hand on a cat's head and it raised its body, undulating as a cat will in response to a caress. At last he reached the rock.

"Are you all right?" he said.

"I'm all right," said Jim. "But Socker . . ."

"I can see Socker," said Willy. He walked toward the two remaining cats and began to talk to them, making inarticulate but friendly, calming sounds, and the cats allowed their muscles to relax and, one by one, stood up and waited for him. Willy continued walking and talking, and they turned and followed him away from the rock. As they passed by Jim they were making grumbling noises in their throats, half purr, half growl.

All the cats were quiet now. Willy walked slowly round the circle of crouching animals, talking, sometimes stroking, occasionally shoving. And the cats permitted it and drew back as he walked, so that when he came full circle there was an appreciable space between them and the rock. Then he turned and came again to where Jim waited over Socker's body.

"How is he?" said Willy. "Have you looked?"

Until that moment Jim had not thought of how much Socker might have been damaged. He had thought only of rescuing him from the cats. Now it occurred to him that it might all have been wasted effort. Perhaps Socker was dead. He had stopped kicking some time before. Jim threw down his stick and bent over Socker's head. Willy crouched on the other side and between them they unclasped the protecting hands. The first sight of his face was something Jim had not been prepared for. He drew in his breath with a hiss. But Socker's eyes were open and he said quite clearly, with a hint of his old aggressive tone, "I could have fought them off. Only for my leg." Then his eyes half closed and his head fell forward again.

Willy said, "Look at his leg, Jim. You know better than me." Willy had never cared to deal with injuries. Even cuts with a pocket knife had turned his face pale.

The leg, bent beneath the body, was difficult to get at and they tried to roll him over and get him off the rock. But as they began to move him he lifted his head and made a sudden sharp sound.

Jim let him down carefully and looked at Willy. "I saw enough," he said. "It's broken. What do we do now, Willy?"

The storm had rolled over to the east and in the west the sky was clear again. The last of the sun flushed the higher ground with lemon-coloured light, but soon the night would be on them. The wind had dropped again and only the wet rocks about them and the dripping vegetation showed that there had been a storm at all. All round in a rough, motionless circle the cats still waited and watched. They no longer crouched with muscles tense, but sat, relaxed but alert. And now they began, one after another, a kind of singing. In the still evening the sound rose and fell, not loud, not excited, but persistent and penetrating, and in it there was a kind of expectancy, as if it was not yet over — as if they still waited for some kind of climax.

After a long time Willy said, "We can't leave him here. We'll have to get him back to the car."

It seemed an impossible job and Jim said doubtfully, "If the cats go . . ."

"The cats won't go," said Willy. He gave a kind of laugh and said, "Like Socker, they think they've got their rights. They don't know I'm going to try to get him away from them."

"Try?" said Jim.

The look Willy gave him was expressionless, but he said, "You know how hard it is to get birds away from Tibs."

"Well then?" Jim did not look at the rows of slit-pupilled eyes that regarded them unwinkingly.

Willy began talking slowly. "I've got to tell you — we could walk away now, you and me, and we'd get back to the clearing without a cat following us. If we try to take Socker with us . . ." He did not go on. There was no need.

"I see," said Jim at last. Then he said prosaically, "We'll never lift him. He'll have to be dragged. We'll have to get him onto something."

13

I N T H E E N D they somehow got him onto two saplings. Jim, walking on eggshells, went through the cats to the edge of the scrub and pulled up the two biggest he could manage. If it had not been for the storm they would never have come out of the baked ground. He broke off the branches but had to leave the roots. The cats started to object when he dragged them back, but Willy made soothing sounds and they did nothing worse than pat at the passing roots and snarl.

They joined the rooted ends with Socker's socks and spread the tops apart, joining them with whatever articles of clothing they could spare. Socker's belt, the strongest thing they had, went across where they judged his shoulders would lie. As a stretcher it was less than adequate, but they had no other and there was no alternative.

Socker, conscious now, watched with a fixed and intense gaze. His silence was still unbroken. There came the time when his leg had to be splinted so that he could be moved. When Jim had found a suitable stick and Willy had torn strips from the bottom of his pants, Socker raised himself on his palms and remained, head up and immovable while they dealt as best they could with the broken bones. Only once, as Jim pulled the knot tight, he opened his mouth and roared. After that he slumped down and they thought he might have fainted, for he made no further move, and when, with great difficulty they rolled him on to the prepared saplings his eyes were closed and his body limp.

When he shouted all the cats sprang to their feet and their tails began slowly lashing. Willy spoke to them for a long time before they sank down to their original positions.

"Now what?" said Willy. The light was fading fast. Socker lay full length between the saplings. They had secured his shoulders, one to each pole. His broken leg was tied to its own sock, which was joining the poles together. It was a kind of shock-absorber and it was the best they could think of.

"Now we each pick up a pole and pull," said Jim. He looked at Socker's solid body, at the slim poles, and thought of the long, rough road to where the car waited, and of the darkness ahead. "Do you think we'll do it?" he said.

"We'll have to try, won't we?" said Willy, and bent to pick up his pole end.

141

Between them they managed to lift Socker just clear of the ground. As the makeshift stretcher took the weight the strips of clothing sagged and the poles bent. But nothing broke.

"Now pull," said Jim. "Slowly."

They pulled together and the two roots, like mopheads, slid slowly across the ground. Socker was moving.

Neither of them spoke, but inside himself Jim was saying, "What about the cats? Willy, what about the cats?" It was a question that would answer itself — now.

When they got the stretcher facing the direction they had to go Willy turned so that he walked backwards. So that he faced the cats. Jim took his pole over his shoulder and pulled forwards. As the stretcher began to slide across the ground the cats, which had been crouching, stood up. Their ears were pricked. Their eyes were on the body of Socker. As the stretcher moved they parted and let it through. But they closed in behind it and followed, and the whiskers of the first cat twitched not six inches from Socker's feet. Once or twice a paw with the claws retracted was stretched out to touch as they went through. But it seemed that for the moment they were content to follow. When all the cats were behind and Willy had been watching them for some time they stopped to let him turn round and take his pole as Jim was doing; the only possible position for a long haul.

As they started off again he said, "If we can keep them off till daylight we'll be right."

Jim was about to ask, "And if we can't?" and realized it was a silly question.

Afterwards Jim could hardly remember the rest of that night. There seemed to be no end to it and often, when they were forced to take one of their many rests he thought that no more effort was possible. Sometimes it was he who got Willy to his feet again, and sometimes it was Willy who jolted him into action. There were times when Socker was sensible, and these were the worst, for there was no preventing the saplings bumping and scraping over the ruts and boulders in the road. Only once, after hours and hours of silence, did he ask them to put him down and leave him.

"I can't take any more," he said, and that was the only admission of defeat Jim ever heard him make.

But they took no notice, knowing he could see behind them the silent, padding ranks of cats. Except for the lighter coloured ones, their bodies were shadows in the darkness.

Many times their rickety stretcher broke in one place or another and they stopped and retied it, and stripped off yet another piece of clothing to make it secure. Even their jeans went at last, and although he was not cold, for the night was windless and his efforts kept him not far from boiling point, Jim had never felt so naked in his life. All those pairs of eyes seemed to prick into his back as he trudged along. He and Willy pulled mostly with their backs bent and the poles over their shoulders, as they had started. It was not long before there were red marks where the poles rested, then blisters, and then the blisters broke and Jim began to wonder if it was they or Socker who were in the most pain. At Willy's suggestion they made pads with little pieces of clothing stuffed with leaves, and these helped, but nothing could take away the pain of the constant rubbing.

There was a time when, without realizing they had done so, they both sank down, the poles across their backs, and slept. But Willy, who seemed to wake by instinct, clambered to his feet just as the first of the cats

143

were stretching their noses towards the stretcher. After that he said they must arrange to sleep in turns, and every hour or so one would lie down for about ten minutes. The waking, after such a brief time was almost more painful than the effort to keep going, but it did enable them to continue. Their progress was slow from the beginning, but, as the night went on, the periods when they did not move at all became far longer than the times when they were making progress.

They had still some distance to go when the cats changed their tactics. Now, as they had that night in the mist, they came up on either side, and wherever Jim looked except straight ahead, there were the silently moving bodies. They did not speak much, but when at last he said, "Is it all right, Willy?" Willy replied, "So far." It was not a reassuring reply.

Perhaps, during the long trek, the cats' fury cooled. Perhaps they looked to Willy for a final satisfaction. Perhaps, being animals, their mood simply changed. But although they crowded round and silently escorted — shepherded even — the struggling cortege they did not during the hours of darkness attack the body they claimed. Day came at last and as its brightness filled the sky the cats began to drop back. Those on either side allowed the stretcher to outpace them. Those whose noses had been almost touching the roots of the saplings now allowed a gap to form. Little by little the gap widened. The force that drove them forward weakened. If either of the boys had had the energy to look behind them he would have seen a cat yawn, and he would have known that the danger, for that night, was over.

Willy and Jim were past looking round. They were scarcely aware the day had come. Their shoulders were on fire. Their legs silently screamed for rest. In all his football playing, swimming, competing life, Jim had never discovered, as he discovered now, that it is possible to drive the body on when every nerve, every muscle, every drop of flowing blood is saying that the end has come. He learnt on this night that it is possible to keep alive only in the very centre of the brain, alert only to drive that part of it that keeps the muscles working. The ache in his limbs, the pain in his shoulder, became part of one sole, simple aim — to keep going.

They reached the clearing at the same moment that the sun, floating effortlessly in the east, rose clear of the trees behind them and flooded the clearing with yellow warmth. As if it had been a signal they both collapsed face down on the dry grass of the roadside. The poles lay across their backs. Socker, unconscious again, lay between the poles, his face to the morning sky. The cats had gone.

The car, its black surface shining in the sunlight, stood solitary in the middle of the clearing. The storm and the night had passed over it and left it unscathed. But within, or about it, there was no sign of life. For the time being the problem of the car and its occupant did not disturb the sleep of the stretcher-bearers.

The heat of the midday sun and a desperate thirst woke them both at last. Jim woke first because to the discomfort of these was added an acute pain in his left arm. He woke remembering that there had, in another and distant lifetime, been a cat hanging onto that arm. He lifted his head and sneezed. His face was stuck all over with dust and bits of grass. The sudden jerk of the sneeze made him aware of the pain in his shoulder. As he started to turn over, moving slowly and with great effort, all the muscles of his body told him they had been greatly abused and had no wish to be made use of again. He groaned.

145

Beside him Willy raised a face so pale, so lifeless with its staring, unseeing eyes, that he could have been dead. But he had moved and now said hoarsely, "Jim." Then his head fell forward again into the grass.

Little by little as Jim moved himself by inches into a sitting position he began to recall the events of the night. At first he had wondered without emotion why there should be somebody's head lying between the poles beside his knees. Then he remembered that it was Socker's head. The black hair brushed his bare leg. The eyes, half open, stared at the sky. Memory and rational thought filtered into his brain together. He wondered if Socker were dead, for there were flies on his face, and his whole body, with the roughly splinted leg, lay motionless. But as he watched, the bitten, blood-encrusted lips began to move and a kind of muttering emerged. For the time being Jim felt nothing at all, neither pity nor anger nor fear. But his brain told him that Socker must be moved into the shade and that they must all, somehow, drink.

"Willy," he said. "Willy, come on." and Willy stirred at his voice, moved and focussed his eyes.

Together, with infinite effort and over an endless period of time they pulled Socker over to the trees. There was still the urgent problem of water. There would still be water in the car, but the car was a long way off. Pulling Socker into the shade was as much as either Jim or Willy could do. They had flopped down beside the stretcher and Willy seemed already to have gone to sleep again. Jim heaved himself on to his good elbow and looked at the car. The door was open now and Kevin seemed to be moving about. He must have been looking for them, but would not have thought to look near the trees on this side of the clearing. His eyes would have been on the road, where they had last been visible to him.

"Kevin!" The sound that emerged from Jim's throat was not what he had expected. It did not sound like his own voice, and he hoped, weak and hoarse as it was, that it would reach as far as Kevin. He tried again. "Kevin!" This time it was a little louder and this time he saw Kevin spin round, shade his eyes against the sun with his good hand and peer across the clearing. He had no energy to call again.

He had dropped off to sleep by the time Kevin came stumbling towards him. It was not so much the wish to help as the wish to end his solitude that had at last driven him from the safety of the car, out across the desolation of the small clearing. Jim woke a second time to find Kevin's face hovering, anxious, alarmed, over his own.

"Go away, Kevin," he said irritably. Then he remembered, and sat up quickly. His arm hurt and round his head the sky rotated. He blinked, gasped, and closed his eyes. When he opened them cautiously the heavens had stopped swirling and Kevin's face was still there.

"My hand hurts," said Kevin. "I thought you were never coming back." He appeared not to have noticed Socker at all. His whole attention was on the one conscious member of the party.

Jim was still only capable of thinking of one thing at a time, and he said, "Go and bring us the water from the car. Quick. And don't spill it."

At once Kevin said, "I can't. I'm sick. My hand hurts."

"If you don't go and get it straight away we'll go away and leave you and never come back." He meant it. Kevin was of no importance and he was too tired to talk. He lay down again and shut his eyes. He had no idea how much time had passed before he opened them again, but when he did it was to find Willy beside him with a mug of water.

"Kevin got it in the end," said Willy. "Here."

The water revived them all. Even Socker stopped muttering, opened his eyes and said, "Thanks." The sun was now in the west and their piece of shade had gone. The last of the journey — back to the car — had to be made. They forced Kevin to help with his one good hand, and Socker, conscious during the whole performance, hung on to the saplings until the knuckles showed white, and made no sound. They got him on to the back seat somehow and then, after resting again, found themselves some food.

When they felt strong enough Willy and Jim went to the creek together to fetch as much water as they could carry. Moving was still painful and Jim, seeing no reason to do so, had said nothing about his arm. They spoke hardly at all, but both knew that, well or ill, they must now go for help. Willy's way over the log would have to be used, and quickly.

They let Socker sleep again until a twinge of pain woke him. Then Jim bathed his blood-encrusted face, and was relieved to find less damage than he had expected. He looked also at Kevin's hand, bathed it once again and wrapped it up. It seemed at least no worse.

Socker said practically nothing. His eyes followed Jim and Willy as they moved about, but he neither complained nor demanded. All that time Jim afterwards only remembered his speaking once. And then it was something he had said before.

"I could have fought them off, only for my leg."

And Willy said, "You couldn't have fought them off forever. It would have taken a little longer, that's all."

148

Kevin began to ask questions and was told briefly what had happened. When he asked for details they told him to shut up. They didn't want to remember, they said. Not yet.

The sun had set and the light was thickening in the clearing when Willy opened the car door by Socker's head, sat himself down on the ground beside it and beckoned Jim. Kevin already occupied the whole of the front seat. Jim sat down beside Willy. Socker lay partly on his side, his head propped on the clothes that had become torn on the way up the hill and were no more use as garments. Jim and Willy wore their jeans again, but Jim's shirt had gone forever and he was bare from the waist up. He wrapped his arms round his chest. The wounds round his elbow were very small and had not bled much, and only he knew how deep they had gone. Socker's eyes were open and resting on his two kidnap victims. There was no self-pity in them, nor any kind of plea, only somewhere behind the tired shadows the same unspoken question.

It was Willy who spoke first. "Jim and me'll go for help."

At once Kevin said, "No."

Willy slowly turned to look at him. "No? Do you reckon to go, Kevin?"

"I can't. How can I with me hand? But you can't both go and leave Sock and me. Tell them, Sock. They can't."

When he had quite finished Willy said, "Socker isn't telling anyone. I'm telling now. Jim and me are going —"

"I'm coming with you." He glanced at Socker as he said it. Willy gave him time to think, and at last he mumbled, "OK. I'll stay."

"We'll stay tonight," Willy continued. "We've got to have rest and we'll need daylight to get over the river."

149

Socker still had not spoken, but now he stared hard at Willy and his eyebrows rose. Willy nodded. "There is a way, Socker, but why should I tell you?"

Jim knew there was one question Socker would want to ask and he answered it for him. "We'll get you water, and Willy will tell Kevin how to find the creek, and we'll leave food and water where you can reach it, Socker, behind the back seat."

"We'll come back with help as soon as we can," said Willy. "And when we come — that's the thing." He stopped and looked to see if Socker was attending. "Socker, when we come, what are we going to say?" Jim noticed even then that he did not say, "If we come."

There was a long pause, and it was broken by Kevin when at last he understood the meaning of what Willy was saying. "You won't tell 'em," he said. "You won't tell 'em, will you?"

"Why not?" said Willy. "We've got a right, haven't we?" and he looked full at Socker as he said it.

"You can't. You can't do that. We can't do with any more." Kevin's voice was rising.

Socker uttered his first words for a long time. "Shut up," he said faintly. His eyes were on Willy's face and Jim saw him nod his head with an effort as he said, "You got the right."

It seemed to satisfy Willy, for he leaned closer, putting his face near Socker's. "I'll make a bargain with you, Socker. Jim and me won't take the right. We won't say you kidnapped us — if you don't say anything about the cats."

Even Kevin had nothing to say, but in the silence that followed Socker's voice came like a breath. "Why not?" Jim could have sworn it was surprise that made him say it.

"I don't have to tell you why not, Socker, and you

wouldn't understand. But if it suits you, that'll be the bargain."

Socker made a movement, and Jim jumped up. But he was holding out his hand, and Willy took it and held it for a moment before putting it carefully back on his good thigh. Jim thought it was more in the meeting of the eyes than in the handshake that the bond was sealed. But they had both forgotten something, and he said, "What about Kevin? Kevin'll never keep his mouth shut."

"I will — I will," said Kevin. "If you don't tell."

"I think Socker will make him," said Willy. "But even if anything slips out, who'll believe him?" And Jim had never before heard just that note of scorn in Willy's voice.

CHAPTER

14

JIM HAD UNDERSTOOD they would wait until daylight, but it was in the dregs of night that Willy shook his arm gently. It was the arm with the bite and it woke him at once. Willy bent down and whispered, "We'll go now while they're both asleep. Kevin won't know which way we've gone — just in case he thinks of following."

Getting away was as easy as that.

They never knew whether Socker was asleep or not, but it made no difference. He had to be left to take his chance, and the sooner they went the sooner they would be back.

152

They were half a mile away when the dawn broke, and there was no more reason for caution. No one could hear them now. It was a windy dawn, clear and crisp, and when the sun appeared the galahs and cockatoos once again took to the air, wheeling and shrieking. This time the movement, the noise, the tremendous confidence they were expressing in the new day acted on Jim like a stimulus. He forgot his aching arm, he forgot the weight of his tired limbs and this time he was indeed lifted — in renewed hope and a kind of exaltation. And he knew that the end of the nightmare was at hand.

There was a great deal to talk about, but for the moment all their energy was directed towards getting through the scrub and over the river. Both knew that Socker could not be left with safety for too long, and neither knew what Kevin might do if pressed too far. He, too, could be dangerous to Socker. They hurried on silently, Willy leading and Jim on his heels. And after a time, when it seemed to Jim that they had been going parallel with the river upstream for some time, the ground began to slope and Willy turned, following the slope until they reached the river itself.

Long before they reached it they could hear it roaring and to Jim it was not a sound that suggested easy crossing. Willy stopped at the edge of the trees and, when Jim stood beside him, pointed to where, just beyond a fringe of undergrowth, a faint mist was rising.

"It's the river," he said. "The tree trunk should be about here somewhere."

It was not hard to find, for its roots still stuck up from the ground, helpless, clawing the air. It had been a huge tree and it hung now, bridging the narrow gash dividing two sheer slabs of rock between which the river rushed, white and turbulent. The far bank was slightly lower than the one they stood on, and Jim saw what Willy meant about the drop. The branches of the tree had caught on a protruding rock just below the top, so that the main trunk hung, poised, some distance above the ground. Cats could jump from twig to twig and reach it, but for himself and Willy there would be no return.

"How can we bring them back?" he shouted over the noise of the water.

Willy shouted in his ear, "By the road we came. Someone with a Landrover and a chainsaw will get through in no time." Then he said. "I've sat and watched once or twice. In the evening the cats come. I've often seen them crossing. It's a wide log."

Looking at it, high above that nasty drop, Jim thought that what might be fine for a cat could well be fraught with problems for himself. But he nodded and, not to let Willy down, gave him a bright smile.

"Come on then," said Willy. "Just follow me."

Jim followed round the entanglement of dried old roots, on to the broad bole of the tree, where he stood, temporarily paralysed, and watched the water moving below. Then, still following Willy, he sat down, straddling the trunk and, propelling himself with his good hand and his thighs, began to move forward. The worst moment was when he left the brink of the cliff and moved out, legs dangling, over the sheer drop below. The spray rose round them, settling on their faces, dampening their jeans, and the log was wet beneath them. It was becoming narrower too, and in a way this was better, because if the worst came to the worst they could always hook their feet together below it and clasp it with their arms.

But Willy moved steadily on and Jim moved after him, and gradually the farther end drew near and the

154

worst was over. The feeling of solid ground below was wonderful. They went as far as they could go, and when the trunk divided into branches, and the branch they were on bent with their weight and began to crack, they jumped off. First Willy, while Jim clung tightly to the released branch as it sprang back, and then Jim, and the sudden jolt as he hit the ground and rolled over was a good feeling. But the bump had hurt his arm, and he cried out before he could stop himself.

"Hurt yourself?" said Willy.

"No. Only me arm."

"What's wrong with your arm?"

"Nothing much." No need to bother Willy at a time like this.

But Willy had taken hold of his wrist and was stretching out his arm, and now he saw the small punctures round the elbow. "The cats?" He looked into Jim's face.

"In the fight," said Jim. "A cat hung onto my arm."

Willy, who did not care for such things, looked closely at the marks. At last he said, "Good thing we're on our way," and gently let go the wrist.

Willy led as before and they plunged into the tangle of trees and undergrowth. There was no track here and they had to trust to their sense of direction. But they knew that if they were able to keep to a straight line they would eventually come to the cleared land. Then it was only a matter of finding the nearest house.

"What'll we do when we get to the house?" said Jim.

He had become accustomed to deferring to Willy, and was slightly surprised when Willy said, "I don't know. You say."

From that moment Jim took on the organizing. It was Willy who, at about noon, brought them out of the scrub

155

to where a wire fence — the first fence they had seen for days — led them to an open paddock and thence, following a car track, to a small homestead. It was Jim who took the lead from that moment on. They forgot they were tired and began to go faster.

"If they have a telephone," said Jim breathlessly, "we'll ring Mum and Dad. They'll want to know, and they'll know what to do. If they haven't a telephone we'll ask them to drive us to the nearest one."

"Supposing they don't?" said Willy.

"They will," said Jim. "They could even know we're missing. Did you think Mum and Dad might have called the police?"

"Gosh," said Willy.

Just before they reached the homestead paddock Jim stopped suddenly. "Willy, if we're not going to say we were kidnapped, what are we going to say?"

It was a point neither of them had thought about, and it took some time to clarify. Until they had done so, they did not dare go any nearer to the house. It was not at all easy to think of a reason why they should have disappeared without a word for the best part of a week. Their family life was regular and orderly, and these things did not happen within its protective framework.

At last they hit on a story that their parents might possibly believe. It was that Willy had taken Jim into the National Park to look at —

"What, Willy? What would I be likely to want to see?"

Willy smiled his slow, gentle smile. "You never want to see anything in the bush. Um — would you come for a kingfisher?" Jim shook his head. "A bower bird?" Again Jim shook his head. "No birds." Willy thought for a moment. "A platypus. Would you come for a platypus?"

This time Jim frowned. Then he nodded. "I think I'd come for a platypus. At any rate, Mum and Dad would think I might come for a platypus."

It was decided they had gone to show Jim the platypus that Willy knew of and got lost.

"They'll never believe you got lost," said Jim.

"Well, say it got dark."

So it got dark, and they couldn't find their way back, and Socker and Kevin came along in their car. And they had been out shooting rabbits.

"It's illegal in the park," said Willy. "But we can't help that."

And they picked them up, but coming home the tree was across the road, so they had had to go the other way.

"And there we are," said Jim in triumph. "After that we had a bit of trouble with storms and trying to cross the river, and so we had to go for help." It had to do and, anyway, perhaps it was more likely than the truth.

Because the house faced down the valley they came to it from the back. There was a wire fence separating the vegetable garden from the milker's paddock. The cow was lying down under a tree in the far corner looking no more than slightly surprised at the sight of them. The chewing of her cud was halted for perhaps ten seconds and then resumed. They unlatched the back gate, shut it behind them on account of the cow and walked up between rows of cabbage and spinach. The sight of such orderly domestic activities was tremendously reassuring. What Jim had not bargained for was the effect of their appearance on whoever came to the back door. As they stepped on to the weatherworn boards of the back veranda they saw that the door was open. Through it came a gleam of polished linoleum. Jim leaned forward and knocked at the door, and they stepped back to wait

157

beside it. It did not seem right to be gazing up the hall at whoever would emerge to let them in.

So it was that when Mrs Thistlewood came to the door she did not immediately see them. No one ever came from behind the house, and she was used to seeing people approach from half a mile up the dusty road from the valley. The noise had sounded like a knock, but she had hardly expected to find it had come by human agency. So when she did see them she gave a little shriek, clapped her hand to her chest and took a step back.

"Excuse me," said Jim.

It must have been a reasonable thing to say, for she pulled herself together and came forward again. "What do you want?" she said suspiciously.

It was obvious that they wanted a good deal, but Jim said, "We wondered if we could use your telephone." And, in case she felt like denying that she had one, "We saw the telephone lines, and so we came."

"The telephone?" she said as if they had asked for shooting stars.

"See, our mother will be wondering."

At once the atmosphere changed. Suspicion vanished, apprehension faded, and Mrs Thistlewood looked at them at last as if they were human beings. It registered then that they were human beings in a fairly needy state. "Come in," she said. "Come in at once. I can't *think* how you got into that state."

It was plain sailing after that. She showed Jim the telephone and then went to put the kettle on. "You'll need a cuppertea," she said. Then, looking at their disgusting appearance, "And a wash." Seeing Jim hesitate by the telephone she called from the kitchen, "Turn the handle. Give it a good twiddle. Lift the receiver and tell the exchange your number. Know what it is?"

For a moment he had to think. Then a female voice said, "Number please." And when he gave it, "Where, dear?" When he told her the name of the town she said, "That'll be a trunk call. Does Mrs Thistlewood mind?"

"See, it's the money," Willy hissed in his ear.

But they could not offer to pay, and Mrs Thistlewood did not mind, or if she did she never said so, and eventually the disembodied voice said, "Your number's waiting. Go ahead please."

It was strange sensation, hearing his mother's voice say, "Hello?" very far away. Faint as it was he could hear that it was tired and anxious. When he had said his own name several times, more and more loudly, she lapsed into incoherence. He heard the word "police" a few times. At last she began to ask sensible questions. Was he all right? Where was Willy? Was Willy all right? And, finally, where were they? Jim managed to give reassuring answers to all her questions and then, feeling she would now understand, said, "Mum, we've got to get back quickly. No. No, we're all right. But there's someone else who's sick. No, Mum, not Willy or me. But someone, and we've got to get help, see? Can you come and get us? Quick?"

Then there was a delay while he had to find out from Mrs Thistlewood where, exactly, they were, and how they could be found. It turned out, to their great relief, that there was a new motorway which cut through the ranges far to the south of where they were. "Takes a good three hours off the journey to your town," said Mrs Thistlewood. "Tell your mother to take the right-hand turn after the bridge at Breakfast Creek. It's a dirt road and it'll bring her straight here. It'll only take her about two and a half hours. Took a whole day before."

By now his mother sounded quite lucid, and was making notes. When all seemed clear she promised to come as soon as she'd told Dad and the police.

"You don't have to get the police," Jim shrieked down the telephone. "We're OK."

"Only tell them. Only *tell* them," came his mother's thin voice. "Jimmy, they've been *looking* for you."

In the end it had to be the police. No one could understand why, having at last got home and obviously in a state of exhaustion and with at least one damaged limb probably in need of attention — and only Jim knew how badly it needed attention — the boys doggedly insisted that a Landrover, a chain-saw and a doctor, complete with stretcher, should be found at once, at nine o'clock that night, to set off for the National Park in the scrub. The story they told, of a broken leg and a poisoned hand, with the haziest explanations of how they had occurred, seemed more like the ravings of minds under stress than of hard fact. Their parents, whom they had relied on to believe them without too much questioning, were the hardest of all to convince. Jim had not reckoned with the strong reluctance of parents of lost children to allow them loose again so soon, and under such conditions. Only when the police, who had insisted on seeing them with their own eyes, were prepared to believe their story. They asked for names, and when Jim told them the names of Socker and Kevin the sergeant looked at both him and Willy very strangely, but made no more difficulties.

Having managed to convince the sergeant, the next problem was to persuade both police and parents that it was essential that Jim and Willy should go too. The real

160

reason, as Jim with his eyes on Willy's anxious face, knew well, was to speak for the cats if it should be necessary. The reason he gave, which swung the balance in the end was that they alone knew the way and speed was essential.

They set off at last and took the doctor, yawning but resigned. Their parents were totally at a loss to understand why they could not go home to bed. To their mother nothing seemed as important as this. Jim's bound arm, which now had begun to throb, was another reason why she looked as if she would murder the police sergeant who had agreed to let them come. But policemen more than mothers know when the end of a tether is reached and he told her they would come to no harm. Then the engine started, drowning their mother's furious retort.

"My Jim has already come to harm." She was pulled away from the Landrover by their father as it moved out into the street.

It was a long wheelbase vehicle, to allow for the opened-up stretcher that now lay folded along one side. Willy and the sergeant sat in front; Jim, the accompanying constable and the doctor sat as best they could in the back. It was late in the night by now and the streets were deserted. Cold blue overhead lights shone uninterrupted on the black asphalt and only once was there any sign of life. In front of the car, lit by the headlights, a small black cat scurried across the street. Before he could stop himself Jim cried out. Willy turned quickly to look at him, saying nothing and the constable by his side said, "Black cats are lucky."

They drove on through the night; out of the town into the open paddocks, across the big highway, deserted now, and at last up into the hills. They were forced to go

161

more slowly and the slower they went the more anxious Jim became. He looked at Willy often and wondered how he could remain so still, so calm. He wondered if it was because Socker and Kevin meant nothing to him, but knew this was not true. After all that had happened there was something that bound them all together. But the cats meant more to Willy and he knew suddenly why Willy seemed in no hurry. It was because he *was* in no hurry. If they did not arrive until daylight the cats would be gone. Willy would not want anyone else to see the cats and the later they arrived the better. He thought, not for the first time, that he would never understand Willy.

They reached the fallen tree, and the constable got out carrying the chain-saw, and the peace of the still bush night was shattered with its demoniac chattering. Willy had been right, and it did not take them long to clear a path.

"That's that obstacle overcome," said the sergeant as they drove on, and Jim could tell that this first proof of their story had come as a relief to him.

After that it seemed a long, long way. The winding road climbed on, the trees enveloped them endlessly. Then, at the first shadowy light of morning they came to the old house. Jim and Willy saw it, and both felt a tremor and a jerk of the nerves as they passed the gateway. That it sat there still, aloof, empty, nursing its secrets, just as they had left it, was in some way astonishing. The sergeant did not even notice it and continued on, downhill now, as if no milepost had been passed. It was growing lighter all the time. The night was over, and when they entered the clearing at last it was full daylight and the sun was rising.

Jim saw Willy sit up and lean forward. The black car,

162

still like a cough lozenge, sat solitary in the empty clearing. Nothing moved either inside or outside it.

"Ah," said the sergeant. "Now let's see."

The constable led the way. "Good God," he said. "Look at that."

The outside of the car — roof, hood, trunk and sides — was streaked and scored with scratches. There was scarcely a square inch of the black surface left intact. Willy's voice came quickly. High and penetrating. "He says he bought it like that. He doesn't know how it happened. He got it cheap, see."

The windows were shut tight. The sergeant pushed past the constable and went up to the window. As he did so Jim saw a face rise up inside the car to meet him. It was a distraught, quivering face with staring eyes, and he had to look again before he recognized Kevin. When they opened the door Kevin fell out in a heap and burst into tears.

The doctor gave him an injection and took him to the Landrover. Socker was lying on the back seat still, his face grey and his eyes half closed. But they opened when the sergeant unlatched the door, and Jim saw them roving, searching, scanning each successive face as it loomed up. He did not think that Socker was properly conscious, but when at last he found Willy's face among the others a change came over him. It was as if a last spurt of vitality found its way into his body. While they dealt with his leg, while they began to extricate him from the car, his eyes never left Willy, and there was a look in them that Jim could not read. Willy was watching him too, though he said nothing, and he continued to hold his eyes until the injection took effect and they closed for the last time for that day.

15

IT WOULD NOT BE RIGHT to say Jim never forgot that period of seven days. When a watershed is reached, it is not a question of forgetting or remembering. The injury to his arm, which stopped his sport from that time on, was a reminder, if he had needed one. For him this was a bigger change than the one caused by the lottery win. He learned to live with it because the limitations it caused seemed less important than some other things that he had experienced at the same time. It came as a surprise to him that Willy had not changed at all. He still required protection for the remainder of their time at school. He still disliked

164

crowds of people. Perhaps his absences when he took his bike and went into the hills became more frequent, and it was true that when he joined the Forestry Department his absences grew into months. This was to be expected. But Jim had thought that Willy, after that time, could never be afraid of anything again. He found it was not true.

Not long after it was all over Jim had a long talk with Willy because there were many things that puzzled him. "Willy, that time when the tree fell across the road, and when the river came up so we couldn't get across. And that time the storm came and the cats went for Socker. Did you — did you make it happen?"

Willy said in quite an ordinary voice, "You must be nutty. How could I make a tree fall? And the river had been up for weeks. And the cats —" For a moment he seemed distressed. "I knew there was something that afternoon Socker went. It was the storm. They'd have waited until night otherwise. I should never have let him go."

"You couldn't have stopped him," said Jim. "And the mood he was in he'd have walked on all night anyway. He knew he had to cross the river somewhere."

It was a long time before they saw either Socker or Kevin again. They had both been taken straight to hospital, and Jim had subsequently been taken to a different hospital, and by the time they were well again life had gone on, circumstances had changed, and the happenings of that week had begun to seem, in spite of the marks they bore to show otherwise, more of a dream than something that had actually happened. Each one of them, for his own reasons, wished it had not happened and each was happy to forget it — to believe

165

that perhaps it had really been a kind of dream. When Jim eventually ran into Kevin again it was to find him working in a garage. His new hero and protector was the garage proprietor, whose claim to fame was that he had once played football for New South Wales. Jim knew him and liked him, and it seemed that Kevin, fluid as ever, was likely to form himself into an acceptable mould at last.

They did not exactly run into Socker. But one day when Jim and Willy were walking home together Socker came round a corner and met them face to face. Once again they were on the edge of the town. Once again it was a lonely stretch of road.

"I want to talk to you," said Socker bluntly.

They waited. To Jim he looked the same as he had always looked, tidily dressed, even over-dressed, his hair still crisp, though longer now, his body still strong and compact, his expression still pugnacious, even truculent, his eyes bright — sharp. But for once he could not begin. To fill the gap Jim said, "You're looking OK, Socker. Leg all right now?"

Socker did not answer, but Jim's remark released whatever had been holding him back. He thrust his hand into his trouser pocket and pulled it out clutching a bundle of bank notes tidily held together by a rubber band. He held it out to Willy. "Here," he said. "It's for you."

Willy stepped back as if he expected the notes to explode and stared wildy at Socker. The notes, Jim saw, were of large denominations.

"What's that for, Socker?" he said when he saw that Willy was struck dumb.

To his astonishment he saw Socker's face turn red. He began to talk — gabble even — in his effort to get it

166

said. "You saved my life, Willy and you. You got a right to something for that. I couldn't think what'd be enough — for a life, I mean — and it isn't enough, but I thought, if you'd take it. . . ." As neither Willy nor Jim seemed eager to do so, he went on, "It's good money. I worked for it. Got a job to earn it. I didn't know what else to do."

There was a long silence. Jim was too dumbfounded to think of anything to say, Willy was not in the habit of speaking, and Socker was too embarrassed to continue. The money wavered in his hand.

In the end it was Willy who found the words. "You know we've got enough money now, Socker. We don't need yours. We don't want to take it." Socker's hand, still clutching the notes, fell to his side. "I got to tell you something, Socker. What we did, Jim and me, we didn't do for you. In a way we did, but not exactly. See, we had to get you back so the cats wouldn't — wouldn't . . ."

Jim spoke now. "Willy doesn't want trouble with the cats. The only way to stop it, after what you did, was to save you. That's why we did it."

The flush slowly died out of Socker's face. Its expression was very still. It was no longer truculent and the look in his eyes changed too. They were calm now and it was as if, for once, you could see deeply into them. Then, once more he held out the notes. "I know you don't need them," he said. "But you saved my life and I owe it. You got a right —" Even as he said it something crossed his face. Something worked on those knotted muscles of jaw and mouth. For once his face relaxed and the beginnings of a rueful smile curled round the corners of his lips. "Oh well," he said. "Thanks anyway." He put the notes back into his pocket, turned and walked away down the street. As he walked he limped slightly.

167

Jim and Willy watched him go. Neither spoke, but Jim thought, not for the first time — a cove to follow, if only he were going in the right direction.

After that it all fell a long way into the past. If the memory of that week stayed with Jim at all it was as if during that time another dimension had been added to his life. As if he had gone through a different door — a door he had not known was there.

Later, when he read, as he occasionally did, of large numbers of lambs being killed by foxes on nearby farms, of fowl houses being raided by animals unknown but thought to be foxes, a kind of chill would run through him. And when he read on one occasion that quite a large calf had been torn down he threw the paper to Willy, walked out of the house and wished with all his heart that he could get out and play one good game of football.

168

WILD CATS WARNING IN OUTBACK

GIANT wild cats weighing up to 25 lbs are roaming central Australia and wiping out thousands of native animals and birds.

The cats are running in near-plague proportions, according to Adelaide hunter Mr Bill Hambly-Clark. They are particularly bad around Alice Springs and Woomera, in the far north of South Australia.

"They're absolute giants and they're killing off everything," Mr Hambly-Clark said yesterday.

Most of the cats weigh about 15lbs — with some up to 25lbs — compared with a domestic cat's top weight of about 9lb. They have giant heads and after years in the wild their teeth have developed to a point where they resemble fangs.

"They are domestic cats, of course, but they have run wild and are breeding in fantastic numbers."

Mr Hambly-Clark said that on a recent shooting trip out of Woomera he bagged 15 of the giant cats in one night.

"People just don't realise how much damage they are doing," he said. "Small ground birds, especially quail and plovers, have disappeared from whole areas, while things like lizards and frogs are easy meat for the cats."

"They even climb down rabbit burrows and kill rabbits — a thing foxes are unable to do."

"One of the biggest problems with them is that they have no natural enemies. Foxes and dingoes can't get near them because they are too fast. People in the bush won't harm them because they look at them and think of their tame cats at home."

"But you can take my word for it — they are killers. And they kill for the sake of killing."

"Birds in trees, especially the young in nests, are as safe as houses where foxes and dingoes are concerned. But the cats thrive on these, climbing trees with ease and killing the young."

The cats are even proving a problem close to Adelaide. The South Australian Conservation Minister, Mr Bromhill, has called for a full report of the effects they are having on native birds in the State's national parks.

But there could be a bright side to the problem. A French fur company has made inquiries about killing the cats on a commercial basis.

Inquiries have been made through the Trade and Industry Department in Adelaide, and Mr Hambly-Clark is expecting to hear soon from the French firm's Melbourne agents.

Mr Hambly-Clark said the cat's pelts were top class. "They are among the best I've seen," he added.

"The only problem is the skinning — they've got some of the hardest skins I've ever encountered."

Extract from *SYDNEY MORNING HERALD* 1971